HOWARD PYLE'S
Book of Pirates

Ye Pirate Bold, as imagined by
a Quaker Gentleman in the
Farm Lands of Pennsylvania.

Books by

HOWARD PYLE

HOWARD PYLE'S BOOK OF PIRATES
MEN OF IRON
A MODERN ALADDIN
PEPPER AND SALT
THE RUBY OF KISHMOOR
STOLEN TREASURE
THE WONDER CLOCK

———

HARPER AND ROW, PUBLISHERS
ESTABLISHED 1817

HOWARD PYLE'S
Book of Pirates

Fiction, Fact & Fancy concerning
the Buccaneers & Marooners of
the Spanish Main

From the writings & pictures of Howard Pyle
Compiled by Merle Johnson

HARPER & ROW, PUBLISHERS
New York, Evanston, and London

HOWARD PYLE'S BOOK OF PIRATES

ACKNOWLEDGMENT

For permission to use certain material in this book, courteous acknowledgment is made to *The Northwestern Miller,* through the kindness of Mr. Edgar, for the stories "Captain Scarfield" and "Blueskin, the Pirate," with their accompanying illustrations; The Century Company for the chapter from *Jack Ballister's Fortunes,* together with several illustrations from the book; *Collier's Weekly* for "Dead Men Tell No Tales" and "The Burning Ship"; also to Messrs. Thornton Oakley, Harry E. Townsend, and N. C. Wyeth for sketches which are reproduced here for the first time.

Special thanks are due them all for their ready assistance in making the book a complete representation of Mr. Pyle's work in this special field and in so far worthy of his high position in American art and letters.

CONTENTS

ILLUSTRATIONS

FOREWORD

PIRATES, Buccaneers, Marooners, those cruel but picturesque sea wolves who once infested the Spanish Main, all
live in present-day conceptions in great degree as drawn by
the pen and pencil of Howard Pyle.

Pyle, artist-author, living in the latter half of the nine-
teenth century and the first decade of the twentieth, had the
fine faculty of transposing himself into any chosen period of
history and making its people flesh and blood again—not just
historical puppets. His characters were sketched with both
words and picture; with both words and picture he ranks as
a master, with a rich personality which makes his work individual and attractive in either medium.

He was one of the founders of present-day American
illustration, and his pupils and grand-pupils pervade that field
to-day. While he bore no such important part in the world of
letters, his stories are modern in treatment, and yet widely
read. His range included historical treatises concerning his
favorite Pirates (Quaker though he was); fiction, with the
same Pirates as principals; Americanized version of Old World

fairy tales; boy stories of the Middle Ages, still best sellers to growing lads; stories of the occult, such as *In Tenebras* and *To the Soil of the Earth,* which, if newly published, would be hailed as contributions to our latest cult.

In all these fields Pyle's work may be equaled, surpassed, save in one. It is improbable that anyone else will ever bring his combination of interest and talent to the depiction of these old-time Pirates, any more than there could be a second Remington to paint the now extinct Indians and gun-fighters of the Great West.

Important and interesting to the student of history, the adventure-lover, and the artist, as they are, these Pirate stories and pictures have been scattered through many magazines and books. Here, in this volume, they are gathered together for the first time, perhaps not just as Mr. Pyle would have done, but with a completeness and appreciation of the real value of the material which the author's modesty might not have permitted.

MERLE JOHNSON.

PREFACE

Why is it that a little spice of deviltry lends not an unpleasantly titillating twang to the great mass of respectable flour that goes to make up the pudding of our modern civilization? And pertinent to this question another—Why is it that the pirate has, and always has had, a certain lurid glamour of the heroical enveloping him round about? Is there, deep under the accumulated debris of culture, a hidden groundwork of the old-time savage? Is there even in these well-regulated times an unsubdued nature in the respectable mental household of every one of us that still kicks against the pricks of law and order? To make my meaning more clear, would not every boy, for instance—that is, every boy of any account—rather be a pirate captain than a Member of Parliament? And we ourselves—would we not rather read such a story as that of Captain Avery's capture of the East Indian treasure ship, with its beautiful princess and load of jewels (which gems he sold by the handful, history sayeth, to a Bristol merchant), than, say, one of Bishop Atterbury's sermons, or the goodly Master Robert Boyle's religious romance of "Theodora and Didymus"?

It is to be apprehended that to the unregenerate nature of most of us there can be but one answer to such a query.

In the pleasurable warmth the heart feels in answer to tales of derring-do Nelson's battles are all mightily interesting, but, even in spite of their romance of splendid courage, I fancy that the majority of us would rather turn back over the leaves of history to read how Drake captured the Spanish treasure ship in the South Sea, and of how he divided such a quantity of booty in the Island of Plate (so named because of the tremendous dividend there declared) that it had to be measured in quart bowls, being too considerable to be counted.

Courage and daring, no matter how mad and ungodly, have always a redundancy of *vim* and life to recommend them to the nether man that lies within us, and no doubt his desperate courage, his battle against the tremendous odds of all the civilized world of law and order, have had much to do in making a popular hero of our friend of the black flag. But it is not altogether courage and daring that endear him to our hearts. There is another and perhaps a greater kinship in that lust for wealth that makes one's fancy revel more pleasantly in the story of the division of treasure in the pirate's island retreat, the hiding of his godless gains somewhere in the sandy stretch of tropic beach, there to remain hidden until the time should come to rake the doubloons up again and to spend them like a lord in polite society, than in the most thrilling tales of his wonderful escapes from commissioned cruisers through tortuous channels between the coral reefs.

And what a life of adventure is his, to be sure! A life of constant alertness, constant danger, constant escape! An ocean Ishmaelite, he wanders forever aimlessly, homelessly; now unheard of for months, now careening his boat on some lonely uninhabited shore, now appearing suddenly to swoop down on some merchant vessel with rattle of musketry, shouting, yells, and a hell of unbridled passions let loose to rend and tear. What a Carlislean hero! What a setting of blood and lust and flame and rapine for such a hero!

Piracy, such as was practiced in the flower of its days—that is, during the early eighteenth century—was no sudden growth. It was an evolution, from the semilawful buccaneering of the sixteenth century, just as buccaneering was upon its part, in a certain sense, an evolution from the unorganized, unauthorized warfare of the Tudor period.

For there was a deal of piratical smack in the anti-Spanish ventures of Elizabethan days. Many of the adventurers—of the Sir Francis Drake school, for instance—actually overstepped again and again the bounds of international law, entering into the realms of *de facto* piracy. Nevertheless, while their doings were not recognized officially by the government, the perpetrators were neither punished nor reprimanded for their excursions against Spanish commerce at home or in the West Indies; rather were they commended, and it was considered not altogether a discreditable thing for men to get rich upon the spoils taken from Spanish galleons in times of nominal peace. Many of the most reputable citizens and merchants of London, when they felt that the queen failed in her duty of pushing the fight against the great Catholic Power, fitted out fleets upon their own account and sent them to levy good Protestant war of a private nature upon the Pope's anointed.

Some of the treasures captured in such ventures were immense, stupendous, unbelievable. For an example, one can hardly credit the truth of the "purchase" gained by Drake in the famous capture of the plate ship in the South Sea.

One of the old buccaneer writers of a century later says: "The Spaniards affirm to this day that he took at that time twelve score tons of plate and sixteen bowls of coined money a man (his number being then forty-five men in all), insomuch that they were forced to heave much of it overboard, because his ship could not carry it all."

Maybe this was a very greatly exaggerated statement put by the author and his Spanish authorities, nevertheless there was enough truth in it to prove very conclusively to the bold minds of the age that tremendous profits—"purchases" they called them—were to be made from piracy. The Western World is filled with the names of daring mariners of those old days, who came flitting across the great trackless ocean in their little tublike boats of a few hundred tons burden, partly to explore unknown seas, partly—largely, perhaps—in pursuit of Spanish treasure: Frobisher, Davis, Drake, and a score of others.

In this left-handed war against Catholic Spain many of the adventurers were, no doubt, stirred and incited by a grim, Calvinistic, puritanical zeal for Protestantism. But equally beyond doubt the gold and silver and plate of the "Scarlet Woman" had much to do with the persistent energy with which these hardy mariners braved the mysterious, unknown terrors of the great unknown ocean that stretched away to the sunset, there in faraway waters to attack the huge, unwieldy, treasure-laden galleons that sailed up and down the Caribbean Sea and through the Bahama Channel.

Of all ghastly and terrible things old-time religious war was the most ghastly and terrible. One can hardly credit nowadays the cold, callous cruelty of those times. Generally death was the least penalty that capture entailed. When the Spaniards made prisoners of the English, the Inquisition took them in hand, and what that meant all the world knows. When the English captured a Spanish vessel the prisoners were tortured, either for the sake of revenge or to compel them to disclose where treasure lay hidden. Cruelty begat cruelty, and it would be hard to say whether the Anglo-Saxon or the Latin showed himself to be most proficient in torturing his victim.

When Cobham, for instance, captured the Spanish ship in the Bay of Biscay, after all resistance was over and the heat of the battle had cooled, he ordered his crew to bind the captain and all of the crew and every Spaniard aboard—whether in arms or not—to sew them up in the mainsail and to fling them overboard. There were some twenty dead bodies in the sail when a few days later it was washed up on the shore.

Of course such acts were not likely to go unavenged, and many an innocent life was sacrificed to pay the debt of Cobham's cruelty.

Nothing could be more piratical than all this. Nevertheless, as was said, it was winked at, condoned, if not sanctioned, by the law; and it was not beneath people of family and respectability to take part in it. But by and by Protestantism and Catholicism began to be at somewhat less deadly enmity with each other; religious wars were still far enough from being ended, but the scabbard of the sword was no longer flung away when the blade was drawn. And so followed a time of nominal peace, and a generation arose with whom it was no longer respectable and worthy—one might say a matter of duty—to fight a country with which one's own land was not at war. Nevertheless, the seed had been sown; it had been demonstrated that it was feasible to practice piracy against Spain and not to suffer therefor. Blood had been shed and cruelty practiced, and, once indulged, no lust seems stronger than that of shedding blood and practicing cruelty.

Though Spain might be ever so well grounded in peace at home, in the West Indies she was always at war with the whole world—English, French, Dutch. It was almost a matter of life or death with her to keep her hold upon the New World.

At home she was bankrupt and, upon the earthquake of the Reformation, her power was already beginning to totter and to crumble to pieces. America was her treasure house, and from it alone could she hope to keep her leaking purse full of gold and silver. So it was that she strove strenuously, desperately, to keep out the world from her American possessions—a bootless task, for the old order upon which her power rested was broken and crumbled forever. But still she strove, fighting against fate, and so it was that in the tropical America it was one continual war between her and all the world. Thus it came that, long after piracy ceased to be allowed at home, it continued in those far-away seas with unabated vigor, recruiting to its service all that lawless malign element which gathers together in every newly opened country where the only law is lawlessness, where might is right and where a living is to be gained with no more trouble than cutting a throat.

HOWARD PYLE'S
Book of Pirates

I

BUCCANEERS AND MAROONERS
OF THE SPANISH MAIN

JUST above the northwestern shore of the old
island of Hispaniola—the Santo Domingo of
our day—and separated from it only by a
narrow channel of some five or six miles in
width, lies a queer little hunch of an island, known, because of
a distant resemblance to that animal, as the Tortuga de Mar,
or sea turtle. It is not more than twenty miles in length by
perhaps seven or eight in breadth; it is only a little spot of
land, and as you look at it upon the map a pin's head would

almost cover it; yet from that spot, as from a center of inflammation, a burning fire of human wickedness and ruthlessness and lust overran the world, and spread terror and death throughout the Spanish West Indies, from St. Augustine to the island of Trinidad, and from Panama to the coasts of Peru.

About the middle of the seventeenth century certain French adventurers set out from the fortified island of St. Christopher in longboats and hoys, directing their course to the westward, there to discover new islands. Sighting Hispaniola "with abundance of joy," they landed, and went into the country, where they found great quantities of wild cattle, horses, and swine.

Now vessels on the return voyage to Europe from the West Indies needed revictualing, and food, especially flesh, was at a premium in the islands of the Spanish Main; wherefore a great profit was to be turned in preserving beef and pork, and selling the flesh to homeward-bound vessels.

The northwestern shore of Hispaniola, lying as it does at the eastern outlet of the old Bahama Channel, running between the island of Cuba and the great Bahama Banks, lay almost in the very main stream of travel. The pioneer Frenchmen were not slow to discover the double advantage to be reaped from the wild cattle that cost them nothing to procure, and a market for the flesh ready found for them. So down upon Hispaniola they came by boatloads and shiploads, gathering like a swarm of mosquitoes, and overrunning the whole western end of the island. There they established themselves, spending the time alternately in hunting the wild cattle and buccanning[1] the meat, and squandering their hardly earned gains in wild debauchery, the opportunities for which were never lacking in the Spanish West Indies.

[1] Buccanning, by which the "buccaneers" gained their name, was a process of curing thin strips of meat by salting, smoking, and drying in the sun.

2

At first the Spaniards thought nothing of the few travel-worn Frenchmen who dragged their longboats and hoys up on the beach, and shot a wild bullock or two to keep body and soul together; but when the few grew to dozens, and the dozens to scores, and the scores to hundreds, it was a very different matter, and wrathful grumblings and mutterings began to be heard among the original settlers.

But of this the careless buccaneers thought never a whit, the only thing that troubled them being the lack of a more convenient shipping point than the main island afford them.

This lack was at last filled by a party of hunters who ventured across the narrow channel that separated the main island from Tortuga. Here they found exactly what they needed— a good harbor, just at the junction of the Windward Channel with the old Bahama Channel—a spot where four-fifths of the Spanish-Indian trade would pass by their very wharves.

There were a few Spaniards upon the island, but they were a quiet folk, and well disposed to make friends with the strangers; but when more Frenchmen and still more Frenchmen crossed the narrow channel, until they overran the Tortuga and turned it into one great curing house for the beef which they shot upon the neighboring island, the Spaniards grew restive over the matter, just as they had done upon the larger island.

Accordingly, one fine day there came half a dozen great boatloads of armed Spaniards, who landed upon the Turtle's Back and sent the Frenchmen flying to the woods and fastnesses of rocks as the chaff flies before the thunder gust. That night the Spaniards drank themselves mad and shouted themselves hoarse over their victory, while the beaten Frenchmen sullenly paddled their canoes back to the main island again, and the Sea Turtle was Spanish once more.

But the Spaniards were not contented with such a petty

3

triumph as that of sweeping the island of Tortuga free from the obnoxious strangers; down upon Hispaniola they came, flushed with their easy victory, and determined to root out every Frenchman, until not one single buccaneer remained. For a time they had an easy thing of it, for each French hunter roamed the woods by himself, with no better company than his half-wild dogs, so that when two or three Spaniards would meet such a one, he seldom if ever came out of the woods again, for even his resting place was lost.

But the very success of the Spaniards brought their ruin along with it, for the buccaneers began to combine together for self-protection, and out of that combination arose a strange union of lawless man with lawless man, so near, so close, that it can scarce be compared to any other than that of husband and wife. When two entered upon this comradeship, articles were drawn up and signed by both parties, a common stock was made of all their possessions, and out into the woods they went to seek their fortunes; thenceforth they were as one man; they lived together by day, they slept together by night; what one suffered, the other suffered; what one gained, the other gained. The only separation that came betwixt them was death, and then the survivor inherited all that the other left. And now it was another thing with Spanish buccaneer hunting, for two buccaneers, reckless of life, quick of eye, and true of aim, were worth any half dozen of Spanish islanders.

By and by, as the French became more strongly organized for mutual self-protection, they assumed the offensive. Then down they came upon Tortuga, and now it was the turn of the Spanish to be hunted off the island like vermin, and the turn of the French to shout their victory.

Having firmly established themselves, a governor was sent to the French of Tortuga, one M. le Passeur, from the island of St. Christopher; the Sea Turtle was fortified, and colonists, consisting of men of doubtful character and women of whose character there could be no doubt whatever, began pouring in upon the island, for it was said that the buccaneers thought no more of a doubloon than of a Lima bean, so that this was the place for the brothel and the brandy shop to reap their golden harvest, and the island remained French.

Hitherto the Tortugans had been content to gain as much as possible from the homeward-bound vessels through the orderly channels of legitimate trade. It was reserved for Pierre le Grand to introduce piracy as a quicker and more easy road to wealth than the semihonest exchange they had been used to practice.

Gathering together eight-and-twenty other spirits as hardy and reckless as himself, he put boldly out to sea in a boat hardly large enough to hold his crew, and running down the Windward Channel and out into the Caribbean Sea, he lay in wait for such a prize as might be worth the risks of winning.

For a while their luck was steadily against them; their provisions and water began to fail, and they saw nothing before them but starvation or a humiliating return. In this extremity they sighted a Spanish ship belonging to a "flota" which had become separated from her consorts.

The boat in which the buccaneers sailed might, perhaps, have served for the great ship's longboat; the Spaniards outnumbered them three to one, and Pierre and his men were armed only with pistols and cutlasses; nevertheless this was their one and their only chance, and they determined to take the Spanish ship or to die in the attempt. Down upon the Spaniard they bore through the dusk of the night, and giving orders to the "chirurgeon" to scuttle their craft under them as they were leaving it, they swarmed up the side of the unsuspecting ship and upon its decks in a torrent—pistol in one hand and cutlass in the other. A part of them ran to the gun

5

room and secured the arms and ammunition, pistoling or cutting down all such as stood in their way or offered opposition; the other party burst into the great cabin at the heels of Pierre le Grand, found the captain and a party of his friends at cards, set a pistol to his breast, and demanded him to deliver up the ship. Nothing remained for the Spaniard but to yield, for there was no alternative between surrender and death. And so the great prize was won.

It was not long before the news of this great exploit and of the vast treasure gained reached the ears of the buccaneers of Tortuga and Hispaniola. Then what a hubbub and an uproar and a tumult there was! Hunting wild cattle and buccanning the meat was at a discount, and the one and only thing to do was to go a-pirating; for where one such prize had been won, others were to be had.

In a short time freebooting assumed all of the routine of a regular business. Articles were drawn up betwixt captain and crew, compacts were sealed, and agreements entered into by the one party and the other.

In all professions there are those who make their mark, those who succeed only moderately well, and those who fail more or less entirely. Nor did pirating differ from this general rule, for in it were men who rose to distinction, men whose names, something tarnished and rusted by the lapse of years, have come down even to us of the present day.

Pierre François, who, with his boatload of six-and-twenty desperadoes, ran boldly into the midst of the pearl fleet off the coast of South America, attacked the vice admiral under the very guns of two men-of-war, captured his ship, though she was armed with eight guns and manned with threescore men, and would have got her safely away, only that having to put on sail, their mainmast went by the board, whereupon the men-of-war came up with them, and the prize was lost.

But even though there were two men-of-war against all that remained of six-and-twenty buccaneers, the Spaniards were glad enough to make terms with them for the surrender of the vessel, whereby Pierre François and his men came off scot-free.

Bartholomew Portuguese was a worthy of even more note. In a boat manned with thirty fellow adventurers he fell upon a great ship off Cape Corrientes, manned with threescore and ten men, all told.

Her he assaulted again and again, beaten off with the very pressure of numbers only to renew the assault, until the Spaniards who survived, some fifty in all, surrendered to twenty living pirates, who poured upon their decks like a score of blood-stained, powder-grimed devils.

They lost their vessel by recapture, and Bartholomew Portuguese barely escape with his life through a series of almost unbelievable adventures. But no sooner had he fairly escaped from the clutches of the Spaniards than, gathering together another band of adventurers, he fell upon the very same vessel in the gloom of the night, recaptured her when she rode at anchor in the harbor of Campeche under the guns of the fort, slipped the cable, and was away without the loss of a single man. He lost her in a hurricane soon afterward, just off the Isle of Pines; but the deed was none the less daring for all that.

Another notable no less famous than these two worthies was Roch Braziliano, the truculent Dutchman who came up from the coast of Brazil to the Spanish Main with a name ready-made for him. Upon the very first adventure which he undertook he captured a plate ship of fabulous value, and brought her safely into Jamaica; and when at last captured by the Spaniards, he fairly frightened them into letting him go by truculent threats of vegeance from his followers.

Such were three of the pirate buccaneers who infested the Spanish Main. There were hundreds no less desperate, no less

7

reckless, no less insatiate in their lust for plunder, than they.

The effects of this freebooting soon became apparent. The risks to be assumed by the owners of vessels and the shippers of merchandise became so enormous that Spanish commerce was practically swept away from these waters. No vessel dared to venture out of port excepting under escort of power-ful men-of-war, and even then they were not always secure from molestation. Exports from Central and South America were sent to Europe by way of the Strait of Magellan, and little or none went through the passes between the Bahamas and the Caribbees.

So at last "buccaneering," as it had come to be generically called, ceased to pay the vast dividends that it had done at first. The cream was skimmed off, and only very thin milk was left in the dish. Fabulous fortunes were no longer earned in a ten days' cruise, but what money was won hardly paid for the risks of the winning. There must be a new departure, or buccaneering would cease to exist.

Then arose one who showed the buccaneers a new way to squeeze money out of the Spaniards. This man was an English-man—Lewis Scot.

The stoppage of commerce on the Spanish Main had nat-urally tended to accumulate all the wealth gathered and pro-duced into the chief fortified cities and towns of the West Indies. As there no longer existed prizes upon the sea, they must be gained upon the land, if they were to be gained at all. Lewis Scot was the first to appreciate this fact.

Gathering together a large and powerful body of men as hungry for plunder and as desperate as himself, he descended upon the town of Campeche, which he captured and sacked, stripping it of everything that could possibly be carried away.

When the town was cleared to the bare walls Scot threat-ened to set the torch to every house in the place if it was not

8

ransomed by a large sum of money which he demanded. With this booty he set sail for Tortuga, where he arrived safely— and the problem was solved.

After him came one Mansvelt, a buccaneer of lesser note, who first made a descent upon the isle of Saint Catharine, now Old Providence, which he took, and, with this as a base, made an unsuccessful descent upon Nueva Granada and Cartagena. His name might not have been handed down to us along with others of greater fame had he not been the master of that most apt of pupils, the great Captain Henry Morgan, most famous of all the buccaneers, one time governor of Jamaica, and knighted by King Charles II.

After Mansvelt followed the bold John Davis, native of Jamaica, where he sucked in the lust of piracy with his mother's milk. With only fourscore men, he swooped down upon the great city of Nicaragua in the darkness of the night, silenced the sentry with the thrust of a knife, and then fell to pillaging the churches and houses "without any respect or veneration."

Of course it was but a short time until the whole town was in an uproar of alarm, and there was nothing left for the little handful of men to do but to make the best of their way to their boats. They were in the town but a short time, but in that time they were able to gather together and to carry away money and jewels to the value of fifty thousand pieces of eight, besides dragging off with them a dozen or more notable prisoners, whom they held for ransom.

And now one appeared upon the scene who reached a far greater height than any had arisen to before. This was François l'Olonoise, who sacked the great city of Maracaibo and the town of Gibraltar. Cold, unimpassioned, pitiless, his sluggish blood was never moved by one single pulse of human warmth, his icy heart was never touched by one ray of mercy or one spark of pity for the hapless wretches who chanced to fall into his bloody hands.

Against him the governor of Havana sent out a great war vessel, and with it a negro executioner, so that there might be no inconvenient delays of law after the pirates had been captured. But l'Olonoise did not wait for the coming of the war vessel; he went out to meet it, and he found it where it lay riding at anchor in the mouth of the river Estra. At the dawn of the morning he made his attack—sharp, unexpected, decisive. In a little while the Spaniards were forced below the hatches, and the vessel was taken. Then came the end. One by one the poor shrieking wretches were dragged up from below, and one by one they were butchered in cold blood, while l'Olonoise stood upon the poop deck and looked coldly down upon what was being done. Among the rest the negro was dragged upon the deck. He begged and implored that his life might be spared, promising to tell all that might be asked of him. L'Olonoise questioned him, and when he had squeezed him dry, waved his hand coldly, and the poor black went with the rest. Only one man was spared; him he sent to the governor of Havana with a message that henceforth he would give no quarter to any Spaniard whom he might meet in arms —a message which was not an empty threat.

The rise of l'Olonoise was by no means rapid. He worked his way up by dint of hard labor and through much ill fortune. But by and by, after many reverses, the tide turned, and carried him with it from one success to another, without let or stay, to the bitter end.

Cruising off Maracaibo, he captured a rich prize laden with a vast amount of plate and ready money, and there conceived the design of descending upon the powerful town of Maracaibo itself. Without loss of time he gathered together five hundred picked scoundrels from Tortuga, and taking with him one

Michael de Basco as land captain, and two hundred more buccaneers whom he commanded, down he came into the Gulf of Venezuela and upon the doomed city like a blast of the plague. Leaving their vessels, the buccaneers made a land attack upon the fort that stood at the mouth of the inlet that led into Lake Maracaibo and guarded the city.

The Spaniards held out well, and fought with all the might that Spaniards possess; but after a fight of three hours all was given up and the garrison fled, spreading terror and confusion before them. As many of the inhabitants of the city as could do so escaped in boats to Gibraltar, which lies to the southward, on the shores of Lake Maracaibo, at the distance of some forty leagues or more.

Then the pirates marched into the town, and what followed may be conceived. It was a holocaust of lust, of passion, and of blood such as even the Spanish West Indies had never seen before. Houses and churches were sacked until nothing was left but the bare walls; men and women were tortured to compel them to disclose where more treasure lay hidden.

Then, having wrenched all that they could from Maracaibo, they entered the lake and descended upon Gibraltar, where the rest of the panic-stricken inhabitants were huddled together in a blind terror.

The governor of Merida, a brave soldier who had served his king in Flanders, had gathered together a troop of eight hundred men, had fortified the town, and now lay in wait for the coming of the pirates. The pirates came all in good time, and then, in spite of the brave defense, Gibraltar also fell. Then followed a repetition of the scenes that had been enacted in Maracaibo for the past fifteen days, only here they remained for four horrible weeks, extorting money—money! ever money!—from the poor poverty-stricken, pest-ridden souls crowded into that fever hole of a town.

11

Then they left, but before they went they demanded still more money—ten thousand pieces of eight—as a ransom for the town, which otherwise should be given to the flames. There was some hesitation on the part of the Spaniards, some disposition to haggle, but there was no hesitation on the part of l'Olonoise. The torch *was* set to the town as he had promised, whereupon the money was promptly paid, and the pirates were piteously begged to help quench the spreading flames. This they were pleased to do, but in spite of all their efforts nearly half of the town was consumed.

After that they returned to Maracaibo again, where they demanded a ransom of thirty thousand pieces of eight for the city. There was no haggling here, thanks to the fate of Gibraltar; only it was utterly impossible to raise that much money in all of the poverty-stricken region. But at last the matter was compromised, and the town was redeemed for twenty thousand pieces of eight and five hundred head of cattle, and tortured Maracaibo was quit of them.

In the Ile de la Vache the buccaneers shared among themselves two hundred and sixty thousand pieces of eight, besides jewels and bales of silk and linen and miscellaneous plunder to a vast amount.

Such was the one great deed of l'Olonoise; from that time his star steadily declined—for even nature seemed fighting against such a monster—until at last he died a miserable, nameless death at the hands of an unknown tribe of Indians upon the Isthmus of Darien.

And now we come to the greatest of all the buccaneers, he who stands pre-eminent among them, and whose name even to this day is a charm to call up his deeds of daring, his dauntless courage, his truculent cruelty, and his insatiate and unappeasable lust for gold—Capt. Henry Morgan, the bold

12

Walking the Plank

Welshman, who brought buccaneering to the height and flower of its glory.

Having sold himself, after the manner of the times, for his passage across the seas, he worked out his time of servitude at the Barbados. As soon as he had regained his liberty he entered upon the trade of piracy, wherein he soon reached a position of considerable prominence. He was associated with Mansvelt at the time of the latter's descent upon Saint Catharine's Isle, the importance of which spot, as a center of operations against the neighboring coasts, Morgan never lost sight of.

The first attempt that Capt. Henry Morgan ever made against any town in the Spanish Indies was the bold descent upon the city of Puerto del Principe in the island of Cuba, with a mere handful of men. It was a deed the boldness of which has never been outdone by any of a like nature—not even the famous attack upon Panama itself. Thence they returned to their boats in the very face of the whole island of Cuba, aroused and determined upon their extermination. Not only did they make good their escape, but they brought away with them a vast amount of plunder, computed at three hundred thousand pieces of eight, besides five hundred head of cattle and many prisoners held for ransom.

But when the division of all this wealth came to be made, lo! there were only fifty thousand pieces of eight to be found. What had become of the rest no man could tell but Capt. Henry Morgan himself. Honesty among thieves was never an axiom with him.

Rude, truculent, and dishonest as Captain Morgan was, he seems to have had a wonderful power of persuading the wild buccaneers under him to submit everything to his judgment, and to rely entirely upon his word. In spite of the vast sum of money that he had very evidently made away with, recruits poured in upon him, until his band was larger and better equipped than ever.

And now it was determined that the plunder harvest was ripe at Porto Bello, and that city's doom was sealed. The town was defended by two strong castles thoroughly manned, and officered by as gallant a soldier as ever carried Toledo steel at his side. But strong castles and gallant soldiers weighed not a barleycorn with the buccaneers when their blood was stirred by the lust of gold.

Landing at Puerto Naso, a town some ten leagues westward of Porto Bello, they marched to the latter town, and coming before the castle, boldly demanded its surrender. It was refused, whereupon Morgan threatened that no quarter should be given. Still surrender was refused; and then the castle was attacked, and after a bitter struggle was captured. Morgan was as good as his word: every man in the castle was shut in the guard room, the match was set to the powder magazine, and soldiers, castle, and all were blown into the air, while through all the smoke and the dust the buccaneers poured into the town. Still the governor held out in the other castle, and might have made good his defense, but that he was betrayed by the soldiers under him. Into the castle poured the howling buccaneers. But still the governor fought on, with his wife and daughter clinging to his knees and beseeching him to surrender, and the blood from his wounded forehead trickling down over his white collar, until a merciful bullet put an end to the vain struggle.

Here were enacted the old scenes. Everything plundered that could be taken, and then a ransom set upon the town itself.

This time an honest, or an apparently honest, division was made of the spoils, which amounted to two hundred and fifty thousand pieces of eight, besides merchandise and jewels.

The next towns to suffer were poor Maracaibo and Gibraltar, now just beginning to recover from the desolation wrought by l'Olonoise. Once more both towns were plundered of every bale of merchandise and of every piaster, and once more both were ransomed until everything was squeezed from the wretched inhabitants.

Here affairs were like to have taken a turn, for when Captain Morgan came up from Gibraltar he found three great men-of-war lying in the entrance to the lake awaiting his coming. Seeing that he was hemmed in in the narrow sheet of water, Captain Morgan was inclined to compromise matters, even offering to relinquish all the plunder he had gained if he were allowed to depart in peace. But no; the Spanish admiral would hear nothing of this. Having the pirates, as he thought, securely in his grasp, he would relinquish nothing, but would sweep them from the face of the sea once and forever.

That was an unlucky determination for the Spaniards to reach, for instead of paralyzing the pirates with fear, as he expected it would do, it simply turned their mad courage into as mad desperation.

A great vessel that they had taken with the town of Maracaibo was converted into a fire ship, manned with logs of wood in montera caps and sailor jackets, and filled with brimstone, pitch, and palm leaves soaked in oil. Then out of the lake the pirates sailed to meet the Spaniards, the fire ship leading the way, and bearing down directly upon the admiral's vessel. At the helm stood volunteers, the most desperate and the bravest of all the pirate gang, and at the ports stood the logs of wood in montera caps. So they came up with the admiral, and grappled with his ship in spite of the thunder of all his great guns, and then the Spaniard saw, all too late, what his opponent really was.

He tried to swing loose, but clouds of smoke and almost

15

instantly a mass of roaring flames enveloped both vessels, and the admiral was lost. The second vessel, not wishing to wait for the coming of the pirates, bore down upon the fort, under the guns of which the cowardly crew sank her, and made the best of their way to the shore. The third vessel, not having an opportunity to escape, was taken by the pirates without the slightest resistance, and the passage from the lake was cleared. So the buccaneers sailed away, leaving Maracaibo and Gibraltar prostrate a second time.

And now Captain Morgan determined to undertake another venture, the like of which had never been equaled in all of the annals of buccaneering. This was nothing less than the descent upon and the capture of Panama, which was, next to Cartagena, perhaps, the most powerful and the most strongly fortified city in the West Indies.

In preparation for this venture he obtained letters of marque from the governor of Jamaica, by virtue of which elastic commission he began immediately to gather around him all material necessary for the undertaking.

When it became known abroad that the great Captain Morgan was about undertaking an adventure that was to eclipse all that was ever done before, great numbers came flocking to his standard, until he had gathered together an army of two thousand or more desperadoes and pirates wherewith to prosecute his adventure, albeit the venture itself was kept a total secret from everyone. Port Couillon, in the island of Hispaniola, over against the Ile de la Vache, was the place of muster, and thither the motley band gathered from all quarters. Provisions had been plundered from the mainland wherever they could be obtained, and by the 24th of October, 1670 (O. S.), everything was in readiness.

The island of Saint Catharine, as it may be remembered, was at one time captured by Mansvelt, Morgan's master in his

16

trade of piracy. It had been retaken by the Spaniards, and was now thoroughly fortified by them. Almost the first attempt that Morgan had made as a master pirate was the retaking of Saint Catharine's Isle. In that undertaking he had failed; but now, as there was an absolute need of some such place as a base of operations, he determined that the place *must* be taken. And it was taken.

The Spaniards, during the time of their possession, had fortified it most thoroughly and completely, and had the governor thereof been as brave as he who met his death in the castle of Porto Bello, there might have been a different tale to tell. As it was, he surrendered it in a most cowardly fashion, merely stipulating that there should be a sham attack by the buccaneers, whereby his credit might be saved. And so Saint Catharine was won.

The next step to be taken was the capture of the castle of Chagres, which guarded the mouth of the river of that name, up which river the buccaneers would be compelled to transport their troops and provisions for the attack upon the city of Panama. This adventure was undertaken by four hundred picked men under command of Captain Morgan himself.

The castle of Chagres, known as San Lorenzo by the Spaniards, stood upon the top of an abrupt rock at the mouth of the river, and was one of the strongest fortresses for its size in all of the West Indies. This stronghold Morgan must have if he ever hoped to win Panama.

The attack of the castle and the defense of it were equally fierce, bloody, and desperate. Again and again the buccaneers assaulted, and again and again they were beaten back. So the morning came, and it seemed as though the pirates had been baffled this time. But just at this juncture the thatch of palm leaves on the roofs of some of the buildings inside the fortifications took fire, a conflagration followed, which caused the

17

explosion of one of the magazines, and in the paralysis of terror
that followed, the pirates forced their way into the fortifications, and the castle was won. Most of the Spaniards flung
themselves from the castle walls into the river or upon the
rocks beneath, preferring death to capture and possible tor-
ture; many who were left were put to the sword, and some few
were spared and held as prisoners.

So fell the castle of Chagres, and nothing now lay between
the buccaneers and the city of Panama but the intervening
and trackless forests.

And now the name of the town whose doom was sealed was
no secret.

Up the river of Chagres went Capt. Henry Morgan and
twelve hundred men, packed closely in their canoes; they
never stopped, saving now and then to rest their stiffened legs,
until they had come to a place known as Cruz de San Juan
Gallego, where they were compelled to leave their boats on
account of the shallowness of the water.

Leaving a guard of one hundred and sixty men to protect
their boats as a place of refuge in case they should be worsted
before Panama, they turned and plunged into the wilderness
before them.

There a more powerful foe awaited them than a host of
Spaniards with match, powder, and lead—starvation. They
met but little or no opposition in their progress; but wherever
they turned they found every fiber of meat, every grain of
maize, every ounce of bread or meal, swept away or destroyed
utterly before them. Even when the buccaneers had successfully overcome an ambuscade or an attack, and had sent the
Spaniards flying, the fugitives took the time to strip their dead
comrades of every grain of food in their leathern sacks, leaving
nothing but the empty bags.

Says the narrator of these events, himself one of the expedition, "They afterward fell to eating those leathern bags, as affording something to the ferment of their stomachs."

Ten days they struggled through this bitter privation, doggedly forcing their way onward, faint with hunger and haggard with weakness and fever. Then, from the high hill and over the tops of the forest trees, they saw the steeples of Panama, and nothing remained between them and their goal but the fighting of four Spaniards to every one of them—a simple thing which they had done over and over again.

Down they poured upon Panama, and out came the Spaniards to meet them; four hundred horse, two thousand five hundred foot, and two thousand wild bulls which had been herded together to be driven over the buccaneers so that their ranks might be disordered and broken. The buccaneers were only eight hundred strong; the others had either fallen in battle or had dropped along the dreary pathway through the wilderness; but in the space of two hours the Spaniards were flying madly over the plain, minus six hundred who lay dead or dying behind them.

As for the bulls, as many of them as were shot served as food there and then for the half-famished pirates, for the buccaneers were never more at home than in the slaughter of cattle.

Then they marched toward the city. Three hours' more fighting and they were in the streets, howling, yelling, plundering, gorging, dram-drinking, and giving full vent to all the vile and nameless lusts that burned in their hearts like a hell of fire. And now followed the usual sequence of events—rapine, cruelty, and extortion; only this time there was no town to ransom, for Morgan had given orders that it should be destroyed. The torch was set to it, and Panama, one of the greatest cities in the New World, was swept from the face of the earth. Why the deed was done no man but Morgan could

19

tell. Perhaps it was that all the secret hiding places for treasure might be brought to light; but whatever the reason was, it lay hidden in the breast of the great buccaneer himself. For three weeks Morgan and his men abode in this dreadful place; and they marched away with *one hundred and seventy-five* beasts of burden loaded with treasures of gold and silver and jewels, besides great quantities of merchandise, and six hundred prisoners held for ransom.

Whatever became of all that vast wealth, and what it amounted to, no man but Morgan ever knew, for when a division was made it was found that there was only *two hundred pieces of eight to each man.*

When this dividend was declared a howl of execration went up, under which even Capt. Henry Morgan quailed. At night he and four other commanders slipped their cables and ran out to sea, and it was said that these divided the greater part of the booty among themselves. But the wealth plundered at Panama could hardly have fallen short of a million and a half of dollars. Computing it at this reasonable figure, the various prizes won by Henry Morgan in the West Indies would stand as follows: Panama, $1,500,000; Porto Bello, $800,000; Puerto del Principe, $700,000; Maracaibo and Gibraltar, $400,000; various piracies, $250,000—making a grand total of $3,650,000 as the vast harvest of plunder. With this fabulous wealth, wrenched from the Spaniards by means of the rack and the cord, and pilfered from his companions by the meanest of thieving, Capt. Henry Morgan retired from business, honored of all, rendered famous by his deeds, knighted by the good King Charles II, and finally appointed governor of the rich island of Jamaica.

Other buccaneers followed him. Campeche was taken and sacked, and even Cartagena itself fell; but with Henry Morgan culminated the glory of the buccaneers, and from that time they declined in power and wealth and wickedness until they were finally swept away.

The buccaneers became bolder and bolder. In fact, so daring were their crimes that the home governments, stirred at last by these outrageous barbarities, seriously undertook the suppression of the freebooters, lopping and trimming the main trunk until its members were scattered hither and thither, and it was thought that the organization was exterminated. But, so far from being exterminated, the individual members were merely scattered north, south, east, and west, each forming a nucleus around which gathered and clustered the very worst of the offscouring of humanity.

The result was that when the seventeenth century was fairly packed away with its lavender in the store chest of the past, a score or more bands of freebooters were cruising along the Atlantic seaboard in armed vessels, each with a black flag with its skull and crossbones at the fore, and with a nondescript crew made up of the tags and remnants of civilized and semicivilized humanity (white, black, red, and yellow), known generally as marooners, swarming upon the decks below.

Nor did these offshoots from the old buccaneer stem confine their depredations to the American seas alone; the East Indies and the African coast also witnessed their doings, and suffered from them, and even the Bay of Biscay had good cause to remember more than one visit from them.

Worthy sprigs from so worthy a stem improved variously upon the parent methods; for while the buccaneers were content to prey upon the Spaniards alone, the marooners reaped the harvest from the commerce of all nations.

So up and down the Atlantic seaboard they cruised, and for the fifty years that marooning was in the flower of its glory it was a sorrowful time for the coasters of New England, the middle provinces, and the Virginias, sailing to the West Indies

21

with their cargoes of salt fish, grain, and tobacco. Trading became almost as dangerous as privateering, and sea captains
were chosen as much for their knowledge of the flintlock and
the cutlass as for their seamanship.

As by far the largest part of the trading in American waters
was conducted by these Yankee coasters, so by far the heaviest
blows, and those most keenly felt, fell upon them. Bulletin
after bulletin came to port with its doleful tale of this vessel
burned or that vessel scuttled, this one held by the pirates for
their own use or that one stripped of its goods and sent into
port as empty as an eggshell from which the yolk had been
sucked. Boston, New York, Philadelphia, and Charleston
suffered alike, and worthy ship owners had to leave off counting their losses upon their fingers and take to the slate to keep
the dismal record.

"Maroon—to put ashore on a desert isle, as a sailor, under
pretense of having committed some great crime." Thus our
good Noah Webster gives us the dry bones, the anatomy, upon
which the imagination may construct a specimen to suit itself.

It is thence that the marooners took their name, for marooning was one of their most effective instruments of punishment
or revenge. If a pirate broke one of the many rules which
governed the particular band to which he belonged, he was
marooned; did a captain defend his ship to such a degree as
to be unpleasant to the pirates attacking it, he was marooned;
even the pirate captain himself, if he displeased his followers
by the severity of his rule, was in danger of having the same
punishment visited upon him which he had perhaps more than
once visited upon another.

The process of marooning was as simple as terrible. A suita-
ble place was chosen (generally some desert isle as far removed as possible from the pathway of commerce), and the
condemned man was rowed from the ship to the beach. Out

22

he was bundled upon the sand spit; a gun, a half dozen bullets, a few pinches of powder, and a bottle of water were chucked ashore after him, and away rowed the boat's crew back to the ship, leaving the poor wretch alone to rave away his life in madness, or to sit sunken in his gloomy despair till death mercifully released him from torment. It rarely if ever happened that anything was known of him after having been marooned. A boat's crew from some vessel, sailing by chance that way, might perhaps find a few chalky bones bleaching upon the white sand in the garish glare of the sunlight, but that was all. And such were marooners.

By far the largest number of pirate captains were Englishmen, for, from the days of good Queen Bess, English sea captains seemed to have a natural turn for any species of venture that had a smack of piracy in it, and from the great Admiral Drake of the old, old days, to the truculent Morgan of buccaneering times, the Englishman did the boldest and wickedest deeds, and wrought the most damage.

First of all upon the list of pirates stands the bold Captain Avary, one of the institutors of marooning. Him we see but dimly, half hidden by the glamouring mists of legends and tradition. Others who came afterward outstripped him far enough in their doings, but he stands pre-eminent as the first of marooners of whom actual history has been handed down to us of the present day.

When the English, Dutch, and Spanish entered into an alliance to suppress buccaneering in the West Indies, certain worthies of Bristol, in old England, fitted out two vessels to assist in this laudable project; for doubtless Bristol trade suffered smartly from the Morgans and the l'Olonoises of that old time. One of these vessels was named the *Duke,* of which a certain Captain Gibson was the commander and Avary the mate.

Away they sailed to the West Indies, and there Avary became impressed by the advantages offered by piracy, and by the amount of good things that were to be gained by very little striving.

One night the captain (who was one of those fellows mightily addicted to punch), instead of going ashore to saturate himself with rum at the ordinary, had his drink in his cabin in private. While he lay snoring away the effects of his rum in the cabin, Avary and a few other conspirators heaved the anchor very leisurely, and sailed out of the harbor of Corunna, and through the midst of the allied fleet riding at anchor in the darkness.

By and by, when the morning came, the captain was awakened by the pitching and tossing of the vessel, the rattle and clatter of the tackle overhead, and the noise of footsteps passing and repassing hither and thither across the deck. Perhaps he lay for a while turning the matter over and over in his muddled head, but he presently rang the bell, and Avary and another fellow answered the call.

"What's the matter?" bawls the captain from his berth.

"Nothing," says Avary, coolly.

"Something's the matter with the ship," say the captain. "Does she drive? What weather is it?"

"Oh no," says Avary; "we are at sea."

"At sea?"

"Come, come!" says Avary: "I'll tell you; you must know that I'm the captain of the ship now, and you must be packing from this here cabin. We are bound to Madagascar, to make all of our fortunes, and if you're a mind to ship for the cruise, why, we'll be glad to have you, if you will be sober and mind your own business; if not, there is a boat alongside, and I'll have you set ashore."

24

The poor half-tipsy captain had no relish to go a-pirating under the command of his backsliding mate, so out of the ship he bundled, and away he rowed with four or five of the crew, who, like him, refused to join with their jolly shipmates.

The rest of them sailed away to the East Indies, to try their fortunes in those waters, for our Captain Avary was of a high spirit, and had no mind to fritter away his time in the West Indies, squeezed dry by buccaneer Morgan and others of lesser note. No, he would make a bold stroke for it at once, and make or lose at a single cast.

On his way he picked up a couple of like kind with himself—two sloops off Madagascar. With these he sailed away to the coast of India, and for a time his name was lost in the obscurity of uncertain history. But only for a time, for suddenly it flamed out in a blaze of glory. It was reported that a vessel belonging to the Great Mogul, laden with treasure and bearing the monarch's own daughter upon a holy pilgrimage to Mecca (they being Mohammedans), had fallen in with the pirates, and after a short resistance had been surrendered, with the damsel, her court, and all the diamonds, pearls, silk, silver, and gold aboard. It was rumored that the Great Mogul, raging at the insult offered to him through his own flesh and blood, had threatened to wipe out of existence the few English settlements scattered along the coast; whereat the honorable East India Company was in a pretty state of fuss and feathers. Rumor, growing with the telling, has it that Avary is going to marry the Indian princess, willy-nilly, and will turn rajah, and eschew piracy as indecent. As for the treasure itself, there was no end to the extent to which it grew as it passed from mouth to mouth.

Cracking the nut of romance and exaggeration, we come to the kernel of the story—that Avary did fall in with an Indian vessel laden with great treasure (and possibly with the Mogul's daughter), which he captured, and thereby gained a vast prize.

Having concluded that he had earned enough money by the trade he had undertaken, he determined to retire and live decently for the rest of his life upon what he already had. As a step toward this object, he set about cheating his Madagascar partners out of their share of what had been gained. He persuaded them to store all the treasure in his vessel, it being the largest of the three; and so, having it safely in hand, he altered the course of his ship one fine night, and when the morning came the Madagascar sloops found themselves floating upon a wide ocean without a farthing of the treasure for which they had fought so hard, and for which they might whistle for all the good it would do them.

At first Avary had a great part of a mind to settle at Boston, in Massachusetts, and had that little town been one whit less bleak and forbidding, it might have had the honor of being the home of this famous man. As it was, he did not like the looks of it, so he sailed away to the eastward, to Ireland, where he settled himself at Biddeford, in hopes of an easy life of it for the rest of his days.

Here he found himself the possessor of a plentiful stock of jewels, such as pearls, diamonds, rubies, etc., but with hardly a score of honest farthings to jingle in his breeches pocket. He consulted with a certain merchant of Bristol concerning the disposal of the stones—a fellow not much more cleanly in his habits of honesty than Avary himself. This worthy undertook to act as Avary's broker. Off he marched with the jewels, and that was the last that the pirate saw of his Indian treasure.

Perhaps the most famous of all the piratical names to American ears are those of Capt. Robert Kidd and Capt. Edward Teach, or "Blackbeard."

Nothing will be ventured in regard to Kidd at this time,

nor in regard to the pros and cons as to whether he really was or was not a pirate, after all. For many years he was the very hero of heroes of piratical fame; there was hardly a creek or stream or point of land along our coast, hardly a convenient bit of good sandy beach, or hump of rock, or water-washed cave, where fabulous treasures were not said to have been hidden by this worthy marooner. Now we are assured that he never was a pirate, and never did bury any treasure, excepting a certain chest, which he was compelled to hide upon Gardiner's Island—and perhaps even it was mythical.

So poor Kidd must be relegated to the dull ranks of simply respectable people, or semirespectable people at best.

But with "Blackbeard" it is different, for in him we have a real, ranting, raging, roaring pirate *per se*—one who really did bury treasure, who made more than one captain walk the plank, and who committed more private murders than he could number on the fingers of both hands; one who fills, and will continue to fill, the place to which he has been assigned for generations, and who may be depended upon to hold his place in the confidence of others for generations to come.

Captain Teach was a Bristol man born, and learned his trade on board of sundry privateers in the East Indies during the old French war—that of 1702—and a better apprenticeship could no man serve. At last, somewhere about the latter part of the year 1716, a privateering captain, one Benjamin Hornigold, raised him from the ranks and put him in command of a sloop—a lately captured prize—and Blackbeard's fortune was made. It was a very slight step, and but the change of a few letters, to convert "privateer" into "pirate," and it was a very short time before Teach made that change. Not only did he make it himself, but he persuaded his old captain to join with him.

And now fairly began that series of bold and lawless depredations which have made his name so justly famous, and which placed him among the very greatest of marooning freebooters.

"Our hero," says the old historian who sings of the arms and bravery of this great man—"our hero assumed the cognomen of Blackbeard from that large quantity of hair which, like a frightful meteor, covered his whole face, and frightened America more than any comet that appeared there in a long time. He was accustomed to twist it with ribbons into small tails, after the manner of our Ramillies wig, and turn them about his ears. In time of action he wore a sling over his shoulders, with three brace of pistols, hanging in holsters like bandoleers; he stuck lighted matches under his hat, which, appearing on each side of his face, and his eyes naturally looking fierce and wild, made him altogether such a figure that imagination cannot form an idea of a Fury from hell to look more frightful."

The night before the day of the action in which he was killed he sat up drinking with some congenial company until broad daylight. One of them asked him if his poor young wife knew where his treasure was hidden. "No," says Blackbeard; "nobody but the devil and I knows where it is, and the longest liver shall have all."

As for that poor young wife of his, the life that he and his rum-crazy shipmates led her was too terrible to be told.

For a time Blackbeard worked at his trade on the Spanish Main, gathering, in the few years he was there, a very neat little fortune in the booty captured from sundry vessels; but by and by he took it into his head to try his luck along the coast of the Carolinas; so off he sailed to the northward, with quite a respectable little fleet, consisting of his own vessel and two captured sloops. From that time he was actively engaged in the making of American history in his small way.

28

He first appeared off the bar of Charleston Harbor, to the no small excitement of the worthy town of that ilk, and there he lay for five or six days, blockading the port, and stopping incoming and outgoing vessels at his pleasure, so that, for the time, the commerce of the province was entirely paralyzed. All the vessels so stopped he held as prizes, and all the crews and passengers (among the latter of whom was more than one provincial worthy of the day) he retained as though they were prisoners of war.

And it was a mightily awkward thing for the good folk of Charleston to behold day after day a black flag with its white skull and crossbones fluttering at the fore of the pirate captain's craft, over across the level stretch of green salt marshes; and it was mightily unpleasant, too, to know that this or that prominent citizen was crowded down with the other prisoners under the hatches.

One morning Captain Blackbeard finds that his stock of medicine is low. "Tut!" says he, "we'll turn no hair gray for that." So up he calls the bold Captain Richards, the commander of his consort the *Revenge* sloop, and bids him take Mr. Marks (one of his prisoners), and go up to Charleston and get the medicine. There was no task that suited our Captain Richards better than that. Up to the town he rowed, as bold as brass. "Look ye," says he to the governor, rolling his quid of tobacco from one cheek to another—"look ye, we're after this and that, and if we don't get it, why, I'll tell you plain, we'll burn them bloody crafts of yours that we've took over yonder, and cut the weasand of every clodpoll aboard of 'em."

There was no answering an argument of such force as this, and the worshipful governor and the good folks of Charleston knew very well that Blackbeard and his crew were the men to do as they promised. So Blackbeard got his medicine, and

29

though it cost the colony two thousand dollars, it was worth that much to the town to be quit of him.

They say that while Captain Richards was conducting his negotiations with the governor his boat's crew were stumping around the streets of the town, having a glorious time of it, while the good folk glowered wrathfully at him, but dared venture nothing in speech or act.

Having gained a booty of between seven and eight thousand dollars from the prizes captured, the pirates sailed away from Charleston Harbor to the coast of North Carolina.

And now Blackbeard, following the plan adopted by so many others of his kind, began to cudgel his brains for means to cheat his fellows out of their share of the booty.

At Topsail Inlet he ran his own vessel aground, as though by accident. Hands, the captain of one of his consorts, pretending to come to his assistance, also grounded *his* sloop. Nothing now remained but for those who were able to get away in the other craft, which was all that was now left of the little fleet. This did Blackbeard with some forty of his favorites. The rest of the pirates were left on the sand spit to await the return of their companions—which never happened.

As for Blackbeard and those who were with him, they were that much richer, for there were so many the fewer pockets to fill. But even yet there were too many to share the booty, in Blackbeard's opinion, and so he marooned a parcel more of them—some eighteen or twenty—upon a naked sand bank, from which they were afterward mercifully rescued by another freebooter who chanced that way—a certain Major Stede Bonnet, of whom more will presently be said. About that time a royal proclamation had been issued offering pardon to all pirates in arms who would surrender to the king's authority before a given date. So up goes Master Blackbeard to the

Governor of North Carolina and makes his neck safe by surrendering to the proclamation—albeit he kept tight clutch upon what he had already gained.

And now we find our bold Captain Blackbeard established in the good province of North Carolina, where he and His Worship the Governor struck up a vast deal of intimacy, as profitable as it was pleasant. There is something very pretty in the thought of the bold sea rover giving up his adventurous life (excepting now and then an excursion against a trader or two in the neighboring sound, when the need of money was pressing); settling quietly down into the routine of old colonial life, with a young wife of sixteen at his side, who made the fourteenth that he had in various ports here and there in the world.

Becoming tired of an inactive life, Blackbeard afterward resumed his piratical career. He cruised around in the rivers and inlets and sounds of North Carolina for a while, ruling the roost and with never a one to say him nay, until there was no bearing with such a pest any longer. So they sent a deputation up to the Governor of Virginia asking if he would be pleased to help them in their trouble.

There were two men-of-war lying at Kicquetan, in the James River, at the time. To them the Governor of Virginia applies, and plucky Lieutenant Maynard, of the *Pearl,* was sent to Ocracoke Inlet to fight this pirate who ruled it down there so like the cock of a walk. There he found Blackbeard waiting for him, and as ready for a fight as ever the lieutenant himself could be. Fight they did, and while it lasted it was as pretty a piece of business of its kind as one could wish to see. Blackbeard drained a glass of grog, wishing the lieutenant luck in getting aboard of him, fired a broadside, blew some twenty of the lieutenant's men out of existence, and totally crippled one of his little sloops for the balance of the fight. After that, and under cover of the smoke, the pirate and his men boarded the other sloop, and then followed a fine old-fashioned hand-to-hand conflict betwixt him and the lieutenant. First they fired their pistols, and then they took to it with cutlasses—right, left, up and down, cut and slash—until the lieutenant's cutlass broke short off at the hilt. Then Blackbeard would have finished him off handsomely, only up steps one of the lieutenant's men and fetches him a great slash over the neck, so that the lieutenant came off with no more hurt than a cut across the knuckles.

At the very first discharge of their pistols Blackbeard had been shot through the body, but he was not for giving up for that—not he. As said before, he was of the true roaring, raging breed of pirates, and stood up to it until he received twenty more cutlass cuts and five additional shots, and then fell dead while trying to fire off an empty pistol. After that the lieutenant cut off the pirate's head, and sailed away in triumph, with the bloody trophy nailed to the bow of his battered sloop.

Those of Blackbeard's men who were not killed were carried off to Virginia, and all of them tried and hanged but one or two, their names, no doubt, still standing in a row in the provincial records.

But did Blackbeard really bury treasures, as tradition says, along the sandy shores he haunted?

Master Clement Downing, midshipman aboard the *Salisbury,* wrote a book after his return from the cruise to Madagascar, whither the *Salisbury* had been ordered, to put an end to the piracy with which those waters were infested. He says:

"At Guzarat I met with a Portuguese named Anthony de Sylvestre; he came with two other Portuguese and two Dutchmen to take on in the Moor's service, as many Europeans do.

This Anthony told me he had been among the pirates, and that he belonged to one of the sloops in Virginia when Blackbeard was taken. He informed me that if it should be my lot ever to go to York River or Maryland, near an island called Mulberry Island, provided we went on shore at the watering place, where the shipping used most commonly to ride, that there the pirates had buried considerable sums of money in great chests well clamped with iron plates. As to my part, I never was that way, nor much acquainted with any that ever used those parts; but I have made inquiry, and am informed that there is such a place as Mulberry Island. If any person who uses those parts should think it worth while to dig a little way at the upper end of a small cove, where it is convenient to land, he would soon find whether the information I had was well grounded. Fronting the landing place are five trees, among which, he said, the money was hid. I cannot warrant the truth of this account; but if I was ever to go there, I should find some means or other to satisfy myself, as it could not be a great deal out of my way. If anybody should obtain the benefit of this account, if it please God that they ever come to England, 'tis hoped they will remember whence they had this information."

Another worthy was Capt. Edward Low, who learned his trade of sail-making at good old Boston town, and piracy at Honduras. No one stood higher in the trade than he, and no one mounted to more lofty altitudes of bloodthirsty and unscrupulous wickedness. 'Tis strange that so little has been written and sung of this man of might, for he was as worthy of story and of song as was Blackbeard.

It was under a Yankee captain that he made his first cruise —down to Honduras, for a cargo of logwood, which in those times was no better than stolen from the Spanish folk.

One day, lying off the shore, in the Gulf of Honduras,

comes Master Low and the crew of the whaleboat rowing across from the beach, where they had been all morning chopping logwood.

"What are you after?" says the captain, for they were coming back with nothing but themselves in the boat.

"We're after our dinner," says Low, as spokesman of the party.

"You'll have no dinner," says the captain, "until you fetch off another load."

"Dinner or no dinner, we'll pay for it," says Low, wherewith he up with a musket, squinted along the barrel, and pulled the trigger.

Luckily the gun hung fire, and the Yankee captain was spared to steal logwood a while longer.

All the same, that was no place for Ned Low to make a longer stay, so off he and his messmates rowed in a whaleboat, captured a brig out at sea, and turned pirates.

He presently fell in with the notorious Captain Lowther, a fellow after his own kidney, who put the finishing touches to his education and taught him what wickedness he did not already know.

And so he became a master pirate, and a famous hand at his craft, and thereafter forever bore an inveterate hatred of all Yankees because of the dinner he had lost, and never failed to smite whatever one of them luck put within his reach. Once he fell in with a ship off South Carolina—the *Amsterdam Merchant,* Captain Williamson, commander—a Yankee craft and a Yankee master. He slit the nose and cropped the ears of the captain, and then sailed merrily away, feeling the better for having marred a Yankee.

New York and New England had more than one visit from the doughty captain, each of which visits they had good cause to remember, for he made them smart for it.

34

Along in the year 1722 thirteen vessels were riding at anchor in front of the good town of Marblehead. Into the harbor sailed a strange craft. "Who is she?" say the townsfolk, for the coming of a new vessel was no small matter in those days.

Who the strangers were was not long a matter of doubt. Up goes the black flag, and the skull and crossbones to the fore.

" 'Tis the bloody Low," say one and all; and straightway all was flutter and commotion, as in a duck pond when a hawk pitches and strikes in the midst.

It was a glorious thing for our captain, for here were thirteen Yankee crafts at one and the same time. So he took what he wanted, and then sailed away, and it was many a day before Marblehead forgot that visit.

Some time after this he and his consort fell foul of an English sloop of war, the *Greyhound,* whereby they were so roughly handled that Low was glad enough to slip away, leaving his consort and her crew behind him, as a sop to the powers of law and order. And luckily for them if no worse fate awaited them than to walk the dreadful plank with a bandage around the blinded eyes and a rope around the elbows. So the consort was taken, and the crew tried and hanged in chains, and Low sailed off in as pretty a bit of rage as ever a pirate fell into.

The end of this worthy is lost in the fogs of the past: some say that he died of a yellow fever down in New Orleans; it was not at the end of a hempen cord, more's the pity.

Here fittingly with our strictly American pirates should stand Major Stede Bonnet along with the rest. But in truth he was only a poor half-and-half fellow of his kind, and even after his hand was fairly turned to the business he had undertaken, a qualm of conscience would now and then come across him, and he would make vast promises to forswear his evil courses.

However, he jogged along in his course of piracy snugly enough until he fell foul of the gallant Colonel Rhett, off Charleston Harbor, whereupon his luck and his courage both were suddenly snuffed out with a puff of powder smoke and a good rattling broadside. Down came the "Black Roger" with its skull and crossbones from the fore, and Colonel Rhett had the glory of fetching back as pretty a cargo of scoundrels and cuthroats as the town ever saw.

After the next assizes they were strung up, all in a row— evil apples ready for the roasting.

"Ned" England was a fellow of different blood—only he snapped his whip across the back of society over in the East Indies and along the hot shores of Hindustan.

The name of Capt. Howel Davis stands high among his fellows. He was the Ulysses of pirates, the beloved not only of Mercury, but of Minerva.

He it was who hoodwinked the captain of a French ship of double the size and strength of his own, and fairly cheated him into the surrender of his craft without the firing of a single pistol or the striking of a single blow; he it was who sailed boldly into the port of Gambia, on the coast of Guinea, and under the guns of the castle, proclaiming himself as a merchant trading for slaves.

The cheat was kept up until the fruit of mischief was ripe for the picking; then, when the governor and the guards of the castle were lulled into entire security, and when Davis's band was scattered about wherever each man could do the most good, it was out pistol, up cutlass, and death if a finger moved. They tied the soldiers back to back, and the governor to his own armchair, and then rifled wherever it pleased them. After that they sailed away, and though they had not made the fortune they had hoped to glean, it was a good snug round sum that they shared among them.

36

Colonel Rhett and the Pirate

Their courage growing high with success, they determined to attempt the island of Del Principe—a prosperous Portuguese settlement on the coast. The plan for taking the place was cleverly laid, and would have succeeded, only that a Portuguese negro among the pirate crew turned traitor and carried the news ashore to the governor of the fort. Accordingly, the next day, when Captain Davis came ashore, he found there a good strong guard drawn up as though to honor his coming. But after he and those with him were fairly out of their boat, and well away from the water side, there was a sudden rattle of musketry, a cloud of smoke, and a dull groan or two. Only one man ran out from under that pungent cloud, jumped into the boat, and rowed away; and when it lifted, there lay Captain Davis and his companions all of a heap, like a pile of old clothes.

Capt. Bartholomew Roberts was the particular and especial pupil of Davis, and when that worthy met his death so suddenly and so unexpectedly in the unfortunate manner above narrated, he was chosen unanimously as the captain of the fleet, and he was a worthy pupil of a worthy master. Many were the poor fluttering merchant ducks that this sea hawk swooped upon and struck; and cleanly and cleverly were they plucked before his savage clutch loosened its hold upon them.

"He made a gallant figure," says the old narrator, "being dressed in a rich crimson waistcoat and breeches and red feather in his hat, a gold chain around his neck, with a diamond cross hanging to it, a sword in his hand, and two pair of pistols hanging at the end of a silk sling flung over his shoulders according to the fashion of the pyrates." Thus he appeared in the last engagement which he fought—that with the *Swallow*—a royal sloop of war. A gallant fight they made of it, those bulldog pirates, for, finding themselves caught in a trap betwixt the man-of-war and the shore, they determined to bear down upon the king's vessel, fire a slapping broadside into her, and then try to get away, trusting to luck in the doing, and hoping that their enemy might be crippled by their fire.

Captain Roberts himself was the first to fall at the return fire of the *Swallow;* a grapeshot struck him in the neck, and he fell forward across the gun near to which he was standing at the time. A certain fellow named Stevenson, who was at the helm, saw him fall, and thought he was wounded. At the lifting of the arm the body rolled over upon the deck, and the man saw that the captain was dead. "Whereupon," says the old history, "he" [Stevenson] "gushed into tears, and wished that the next shot might be his portion." After their captain's death the pirate crew had no stomach for more fighting; the "Black Roger" was struck, and one and all surrendered to justice and the gallows.

Such is a brief and bald account of the most famous of these pirates. But they are only a few of a long list of notables, such as Captain Martel, Capt. Charles Vane (who led the gallant Colonel Rhett, of South Carolina, such a wild-goose chase in and out among the sluggish creeks and inlets along the coast), Capt. John Rackam, and Captain Anstis, Captain Worley, and Evans, and Philips, and others—a score or more of wild fellows whose very names made ship captains tremble in their shoes in those good old times.

And such is that black chapter of history of the past—an evil chapter, lurid with cruelty and suffering, stained with blood and smoke. Yet it is a written chapter, and it must be read. He who chooses may read betwixt the lines of history this great truth: Evil itself is an instrument toward the shaping of good. Therefore the history of evil as well as the history of good should be read, considered, and digested.

II

THE GHOST OF CAPTAIN BRAND

T is not so easy to tell why discredit should be cast upon a man because of something that his grandfather may have done amiss, but the world, which is never overnice in its discrimination as to where to lay the blame, is often pleased to make the innocent suffer in the place of the guilty.

Barnaby True was a good, honest, biddable lad, as boys go, but yet he was not ever allowed altogether to forget that his grandfather had been that very famous pirate, Capt. William Brand, who, after so many marvelous adventures (if one may believe the catchpenny stories and ballads that were written about him), was murdered in Jamaica by Capt. John Malyoe, the commander of his own consort, the *Adventure* galley.

It has never been denied, that ever I heard, that up to the time of Captain Brand's being commissioned against the South Sea pirates he had always been esteemed as honest, reputable a sea captain as could be.

When he started out upon that adventure it was with a ship, the *Royal Sovereign,* fitted out by some of the most decent merchants of New York. The governor himself had subscribed to the adventure, and had himself signed Captain Brand's commission. So, if the unfortunate man went astray, he must have had great temptation to do so, many others behaving no better when the opportunity offered in those faraway seas where so many rich purchases might very easily be taken and no one the wiser.

To be sure, those stories and ballads made our captain to be a most wicked, profane wretch; and if he were, why, God knows he suffered and paid for it, for he laid his bones in Jamaica, and never saw his home or his wife and daughter again after he had sailed away on the *Royal Sovereign* on that long misfortunate voyage, leaving them in New York to the care of strangers.

At the time when he met his fate in Port Royal Harbor he had obtained two vessels under his command—the *Royal Sovereign,* which was the boat fitted out for him in New York, and the *Adventure* galley, which he was said to have taken somewhere in the South Seas. With these he lay in those waters of Jamaica for over a month after his return from the coasts of Africa, waiting for news from home, which, when it came, was of the very blackest; for the colonial authorities were at that time stirred up very hot against him to take him and hang him for a pirate, so as to clear their own skirts for having to do with such a fellow. So maybe it seemed better to our captain to hide his ill-gotten treasure there in those faraway parts, and afterward to try and bargain with it for his life when he should reach New York, rather than to sail straight for the Americas with what he had earned by his piracies, and so risk losing life and money both.

However that might be, the story was that Captain Brand and his gunner, and Captain Malyoe of the *Adventure* and the sailing master of the *Adventure* all went ashore together with a chest of money (no one of them choosing to trust the other three in so nice an affair), and buried the treasure somewhere on the beach of Port Royal Harbor. The story then has it that they fell a-quarreling about a future division of the money, and that, as a wind-up to the affair, Captain Malyoe shot Captain Brand through the head, while the sailing master of the *Adventure* served the gunner of the *Royal Sovereign* after the same fashion through the body, and that the murderers then went away, leaving the two stretched out in their own blood on the sand in the staring sun, with no one to know where the money was hid but they two who had served their comrades so.

It is a mighty great pity that anyone should have a grandfather who ended his days in such a sort as this, but it was no fault of Barnaby True's, nor could he have done anything to prevent it, seeing that he was not even born into the world at the time that his grandfather turned pirate, and was only one year old when he so met his tragical end. Nevertheless, the boys with whom he went to school never tired of calling him "Pirate," and would sometimes sing for his benefit that famous catchpenny song beginning thus:

> *Oh, my name was Captain Brand,*
> *A-sailing,*
> *And a-sailing;*
> *Oh, my name was Captain Brand,*
> *A-sailing free.*
> *Oh, my name was Captain Brand,*
> *And I sinned by sea and land,*
> *For I broke God's just command,*
> *A-sailing free.*

'Twas a vile thing to sing at the grandson of so misfor-

41

tunate a man, and oftentimes little Barnaby True would double up his fists and would fight his tormentors at great odds, and would sometimes go back home with a bloody nose to have his poor mother cry over him and grieve for him.

Not that his days were all of teasing and torment, neither; for if his comrades did treat him so, why, then, there were other times when he and they were as great friends as could be, and would go in swimming together where there was a bit of sandy strand along the East River above Fort George, and that in the most amicable fashion. Or, maybe the very next day after he had fought so with his fellows, he would go a-rambling with them up the Bowerie Road, perhaps to help them steal cherries from some old Dutch farmer, forgetting in such adventure what a thief his own grandfather had been.

Well, when Barnaby True was between sixteen and seventeen years old he was taken into employment in the counting-house of Mr. Roger Hartright, the well-known West India merchant, and Barnaby's own stepfather.

It was the kindness of this good man that not only found a place for Barnaby in the countinghouse, but advanced him so fast that against our hero was twenty-one years old he had made four voyages as supercargo to the West Indies in Mr. Hartright's ship, the *Belle Helen,* and soon after he was twenty-one undertook a fifth. Nor was it in any such subordinate position as mere supercargo that he acted, but rather as the confidential agent of Mr. Hartright, who, having no children of his own, was very jealous to advance our hero into a position of trust and responsibility in the countinghouse, as though he were indeed a son, so that even the captain of the ship had scarcely more consideration aboard than he, young as he was in years.

As for the agents and correspondents of Mr. Hartright throughout these parts, they also, knowing how the good man had adopted his interests, were very polite and obliging to Master Barnaby—especially, be it mentioned, Mr. Ambrose Greenfield, of Kingston, Jamaica, who, upon the occasions of his visits to those parts, did all that he could to make Barnaby's stay in that town agreeable and pleasant to him.

So much for the history of our hero to the time of the beginning of his story, without which you shall hardly be able to understand the purport of those most extraordinary adventures that befell him shortly after he came of age, nor the logic of their consequence after they had occurred.

For it was during his fifth voyage to the West Indies that the first of those extraordinary adventures happened of which I shall have presently to tell.

At that time he had been in Kingston for the best part of four weeks, lodging at the house of a very decent, respectable widow, by name Mrs. Anne Bolles, who, with three pleasant and agreeable daughters, kept a very clean and well-served lodging house in the outskirts of the town.

One morning, as our hero sat sipping his coffee, clad only in loose cotton drawers, a shirt, and a jacket, and with slippers upon his feet, as is the custom in that country, where everyone endeavors to keep as cool as may be—while he sat thus sipping his coffee Miss Eliza, the youngest of the three daughters, came and gave him a note, which, she said, a stranger had just handed in at the door, going away again without waiting for a reply. You may judge of Barnaby's surprise when he opened the note and read as follows:

MR. BARNABY TRUE.

SIR,—Though you don't know me, I know you, and I tell you this: if you will be at Pratt's Ordinary on Harbor Street on Friday next at eight o'clock of the evening, and will accompany the man who shall say to you, "The *Royal Sovereign* is come in," you shall learn something the most to your ad-

43

vantage that ever befell you. Sir, keep this note, and show it to him who shall address these words to you, so to certify that you are the man he seeks.

Such was the wording of the note, which was without address, and without any superscription whatever.

The first emotion that stirred Barnaby was one of extreme and profound amazement. Then the thought came into his mind that some witty fellow, of whom he knew a good many in that town—and wild, waggish pranks they were—was attempting to play off some smart jest upon him. But all that Miss Eliza could tell him when he questioned her concerning the messenger was that the bearer of the note was a tall, stout man, with a red neckerchief around his neck and copper buckles to his shoes, and that he had the appearance of a sailorman, having a great big queue hanging down his back. But, Lord! what was such a description as that in a busy seaport town, full of scores of men to fit such a likeness? Accordingly, our hero put away the note into his wallet, determining to show it to his good friend Mr. Greenfield that evening, and to ask his advice upon it. So he did show it, and that gentleman's opinion was the same as his—that some wag was minded to play off a hoax upon him, and that the matter of the letter was all nothing but smoke.

Nevertheless, though Barnaby was thus confirmed in his opinion as to the nature of the communication he had received, he yet determined in his own mind that he would see the business through to the end, and would be at Pratt's Ordinary, as the note demanded, upon the day and at the time specified therein.

Pratt's Ordinary was at that time a very fine and well-known place of its sort, with good tobacco and the best rum that ever I tasted, and had a garden behind it that, sloping down to the harbor front, was planted pretty thick with palms

Kidd at Gardiner's Island

and ferns grouped into clusters with flowers and plants. Here were a number of little tables, some in little grottoes, like our Vauxhall in New York, and with red and blue and white paper lanterns hung among the foliage, whither gentlemen and ladies used sometimes to go of an evening to sit and drink lime juice and sugar and water (and sometimes a taste of something stronger), and to look out across the water at the shipping in the cool of the night.

Thither, accordingly, our hero went, a little before the time appointed in the note, and passing directly through the Ordinary and the garden beyond, chose a table at the lower end of the garden and close to the water's edge, where he would not be easily seen by anyone coming into the place. Then, ordering some rum and water and a pipe of tobacco, he composed himself to watch for the appearance of those witty fellows whom he suspected would presently come thither to see the end of their prank and to enjoy his confusion.

The spot was pleasant enough; for the land breeze, blowing strong and full, set the leaves of the palm tree above his head to rattling and clattering continually against the sky, where, the moon then being about full, they shone every now and then like blades of steel. The waves also were splashing up against the little landing place at the foot of the garden, sounding very cool in the night, and sparkling all over the harbor where the moon caught the edges of the water. A great many vessels were lying at anchor in their ridings, with the dark, prodigious form of a man-of-war looming up above them in the moonlight.

There our hero sat for the best part of an hour, smoking his pipe of tobacco and sipping his grog, and seeing not so much as a single thing that might concern the note he had received.

It was not far from half an hour after the time appointed in the note, when a rowboat came suddenly out of the night and pulled up to the landing place at the foot of the garden above mentioned, and three or four men came ashore in the darkness. Without saying a word among themselves they chose a near-by table and, sitting down, ordered rum and water, and began drinking their grog in silence. They might have sat there about five minutes, when, by and by, Barnaby True became aware that they were observing him very curiously; and then almost immediately one, who was plainly the leader of the party, called out to him:

"How now, messmate! Won't you come and drink a dram of rum with us?"

"Why, no," says Barnaby, answering very civilly; "I have drunk enough already, and more would only heat my blood."

"All the same," quoth the stranger, "I think you will come and drink with us; for, unless I am mistook, you are Mr. Barnaby True, and I am come here to tell you that the *Royal Sovereign is come in.*"

Now I may honestly say that Barnaby True was never more struck aback in all his life than he was at hearing these words uttered in so unexpected a manner. He had been looking to hear them under such different circumstances that, now that his ears heard them addressed to him, and that so seriously, by a perfect stranger, who, with others, had thus mysteriously come ashore out of the darkness, he could scarce believe that his ears heard aright. His heart suddenly began beating at a tremendous rate, and had he been an older and wiser man, I do believe he would have declined the adventure, instead of leaping blindly, as he did, into that of which he could see neither the beginning nor the ending. But being barely one-and-twenty years of age, and having an adventurous disposition that would have carried him into almost anything that possessed a smack of uncertainty or danger about it, he contrived to say, in a pretty easy tone (though God knows how it was put on for the occasion):

"Well, then, if that be so, and if the *Royal Sovereign* is indeed come in, why, I'll join you, since you are so kind as to ask me." And therewith he went across to the other table, carrying his pipe with him, and sat down and began smoking, with all the appearance of ease he could assume upon the occasion.

"Well, Mr. Barnaby True," said the man who had before addressed him, so soon as Barnaby had settled himself, speaking in a low tone of voice, so there would be no danger of any others hearing the words—"Well, Mr. Barnaby True—for I shall call you by your name, to show you that though I know you, you don't know me—I am glad to see that you are man enough to enter thus into an affair, though you can't see to the bottom of it. For it shows me that you are a man of mettle, and are deserving of the fortune that is to befall you to-night. Nevertheless, first of all, I am bid to say that you must show me a piece of paper that you have about you before we go a step farther."

"Very well," said Barnaby; "I have it here safe and sound, and see it you shall." And thereupon and without more ado he fetched out his wallet, opened it, and handed his interlocutor the mysterious note he had received the day or two before. Whereupon the other, drawing to him the candle, burning there for the convenience of those who would smoke tobacco, began immediately reading it.

This gave Barnaby True a moment or two to look at him. He was a tall, stout man, with a red handkerchief tied around his neck, and with copper buckles on his shoes, so that Barnaby True could not but wonder whether he was not the very same man who had given the note to Miss Eliza Bolles at the door of his lodging house.

" 'Tis all right and straight as it should be," the other said, after he had so glanced his eyes over the note. "And now that the paper is read" (suiting his action to his words), "I'll just burn it, for safety's sake."

And so he did, twisting it up and setting it to the flame of the candle.

"And now," he said, continuing his address, "I'll tell you what I am here for. I was sent to ask you if you're man enough to take your life in your own hands and to go with me in that boat down there? Say 'Yes,' and we'll start away without wasting more time, for the devil is ashore here at Jamaica—though you don't know what that means—and if he gets ahead of us, why, then we may whistle for what we are after. Say 'No,' and I go away again, and I promise you you shall never be troubled again in this sort. So now speak up plain, young gentleman, and tell us what is your mind in this business, and whether you will adventure any farther or not."

If our hero hesitated it was not for long. I cannot say that his courage did not waver for a moment; but if it did, it was, I say, not for long, and when he spoke up it was with a voice as steady as could be.

"To be sure I'm man enough to go with you," he said; "and if you mean me any harm I can look out for myself; and if I can't, why, here is something can look out for me," and therewith he lifted up the flap of his coat pocket and showed the butt of a pistol he had fetched with him when he had set out from his lodging house that evening.

At this the other burst out a-laughing. "Come," says he, "you are indeed of right mettle, and I like your spirit. All the same, no one in all the world means you less ill than I, and so, if you have to use that barker, 'twill not be upon us who are your friends, but only upon one who is more wicked than the devil himself. So come, and let us get away."

48

Thereupon he and the others, who had not spoken a single word for all this time, rose from the table, and he having paid the scores of all, they all went down together to the boat that still lay at the landing place at the bottom of the garden.

Thus coming to it, our hero could see that it was a large yawl boat manned with half a score of black men for rowers, and there were two lanterns in the stern sheets, and three or four iron shovels.

The man who had conducted the conversation with Barnaby True for all this time, and who was, as has been said, plainly the captain of the party, stepped immediately down into the boat; our hero followed, and the others followed after him; and instantly they were seated the boat was shoved off and the black men began pulling straight out into the harbor, and so, at some distance away, around under the stern of the man-of-war.

Not a word was spoken after they had thus left the shore, and presently they might all have been ghosts, for the silence of the party. Barnaby True was too full of his own thoughts to talk—and serious enough thoughts they were by this time, with crimps to trepan a man at every turn, and press gangs to carry a man off so that he might never be heard of again. As for the others, they did not seem to choose to say anything now that they had him fairly embarked upon their enterprise.

And so the crew pulled on in perfect silence for the best part of an hour, the leader of the expedition directing the course of the boat straight across the harbor, as though toward the mouth of the Rio Cobra River. Indeed, this was their destination, as Barnaby could after a while see, by the low point of land with a great long row of coconut palms upon it (the appearance of which he know very well), which by and by began to loom up out of the milky dimness of the moonlight. As they approached the river they found the tide was running strong out of it, so that some distance away from the stream it gurgled and rippled alongside the boat as the crew of black men pulled strongly against it. Thus they came up under what was either a point of land or an islet covered with a thick growth of mangrove trees. But still no one spoke a single word as to their destination, or what was the business they had in hand.

The night, now that they were close to the shore, was loud with the noise of running tide-water, and the air was heavy with the smell of mud and marsh, and over all the whiteness of the moonlight, with a few stars pricking out here and there in the sky; and all so strange and silent and mysterious that Barnaby could not divest himself of the feeling that it was all a dream.

So, the rowers bending to the oars, the boat came slowly around from under the clump of mangrove bushes and out into the open water again.

Instantly it did so the leader of the expedition called out in a sharp voice, and the black men instantly lay on their oars.

Almost at the same instant Barnaby True became aware that there was another boat coming down the river toward where they lay, now drifting with the strong tide out into the harbor again, and he knew that it was because of the approach of that boat that the other had called upon his men to cease rowing.

The other boat, as well as he could see in the distance, was full of men, some of whom appeared to be armed, for even in the dusk of the darkness the shine of the moonlight glimmered sharply now and then on the barrels of muskets or pistols, and in the silence that followed after their own rowing had ceased Barnaby True could hear the chug! chug! of the oars sounding louder and louder through the watery stillness of the night as the boat drew nearer and nearer. But he knew nothing of what

50

it all meant, nor whether these others were friends or enemies, or what was to happen next.

The oarsmen of the approaching boat did not for a moment cease their rowing, not till they had come pretty close to Barnaby and his companions. Then a man who sat in the stern ordered them to cease rowing, and as they lay on their oars he stood up. As they passed by, Barnaby True could see him very plain, the moonlight shining full upon him—a large, stout gentleman with a round red face, and clad in a fine laced coat of red cloth. Amidship of the boat was a box or chest about the bigness of a middle-sized traveling trunk, but covered all over with cakes of sand and dirt. In the act of passing, the gentleman, still standing, pointed at it with an elegant gold-headed cane which he held in his hand. "Are you come after this, Abraham Dawling?" says he, and thereat his countenance broke into as evil, malignant a grin as ever Barnaby True saw in all of his life.

The other did not immediately reply so much as a single word, but sat as still as any stone. Then, at last, the other boat having gone by, he suddenly appeared to regain his wits, for he bawled out after it, "Very well, Jack Malyoe! very well, Jack Malyoe! you've got ahead of us this time again, but next time is the third, and then it shall be our turn, even if William Brand must come back from hell to settle with you."

This he shouted out as the other boat passed farther and farther away, but to it my fine gentleman made no reply except to burst out into a great roaring fit of laughter.

There was another man among the armed men in the stern of the passing boat—a villainous, lean man with lantern jaws, and the top of his head as bald as the palm of my hand. As the boat went away into the night with the tide and the headway the oars had given it, he grinned so that the moonlight

51

shone white on his big teeth. Then, flourishing a great big pistol, he said, and Barnaby could hear every word he spoke, "Do but give me the word, Your Honor, and I'll put another bullet through the son of a sea cook."

But the gentleman said some words to forbid him, and therewith the boat was gone away into the night, and presently Barnaby could hear that the men at the oars had begun rowing again, leaving them lying there, without a single word being said for a long time.

By and by one of those in Barnaby's boat spoke up. "Where shall you go now?" he said.

At this the leader of the expedition appeared suddenly to come back to himself, and to find his voice again. "Go?" he roared out. "Go to the devil! Go? Go where you choose! Go? Go back again—that's where we'll go!" and therewith he fell a-cursing and swearing until he foamed at the lips, as though he had gone clean crazy, while the black men began rowing back again across the harbor as fast as ever they could lay oars into the water.

They put Barnaby True ashore below the old custom house; but so bewildered and shaken was he by all that had happened, and by what he had seen, and by the names that he heard spoken, that he was scarcely conscious of any of the familiar things among which he found himself thus standing. And so he walked up the moonlit street toward his lodging like one drunk or bewildered; for "John Malyoe" was the name of the captain of the *Adventure* galley—he who had shot Barnaby's own grandfather—and "Abraham Dawling" was the name of the gunner of the *Royal Sovereign* who had been shot at the same time with the pirate captain, and who, with him, had been left stretched out in the staring sun by the murderers.

The whole business had occupied hardly two hours, but it was as though that time was no part of Barnaby's life, but all a part of some other life, so dark and strange and mysterious that it in no wise belonged to him.

As for that box covered all over with mud, he could only guess at that time what it contained and what the finding of it signified.

But of this our hero said nothing to anyone, nor did he tell a single living soul what he had seen that night, but nursed it in his own mind, where it lay so big for a while that he could think of little or nothing else for days after.

Mr. Greenfield, Mr. Hartright's correspondent and agent in these parts, lived in a fine brick house just out of the town, on the Mona Road, his family consisting of a wife and two daughters—brisk, lively young ladies with black hair and eyes, and very fine bright teeth that shone whenever they laughed, and with a plenty to say for themselves. Thither Barnaby True was often asked to a family dinner; and, indeed, it was a pleasant home to visit, and to sit upon the veranda and smoke a cigarro with the good old gentleman and look out toward the mountains, while the young ladies laughed and talked, or played upon the guitar and sang. And oftentimes so it was strongly upon Barnaby's mind to speak to the good gentleman and tell him what he had beheld that night out in the harbor; but always he would think better of it and hold his peace, falling to thinking, and smoking away upon his cigarro at a great rate.

A day or two before the *Belle Helen* sailed from Kingston Mr. Greenfield stopped Barnaby True as he was going through the office to bid him to come to dinner that night (for there within the tropics they breakfast at eleven o'clock and take dinner in the cool of the evening, because of the heat, and not at midday, as we do in more temperate latitudes). "I would have you meet," says Mr. Greenfield, "your chief passenger for New York, and his granddaughter, for whom the state cabin

53

and the two staterooms are to be fitted as here ordered [show-
ing a letter]—Sir John Malyoe and Miss Marjorie Malyoe.
Did you ever hear tell of Capt. Jack Malyoe, Master Barnaby?"

Now I do believe that Mr. Greenfield had no notion at all
that old Captain Brand was Barnaby True's own grandfather
and Capt. John Malyoe his murderer, but when he so thrust
at him the name of that man, what with that in itself and the
late adventure through which he himself had just passed, and
with his brooding upon it until it was so prodigiously big in his
mind, it was like hitting him a blow to so fling the questions
at him. Nevertheless, he was able to reply, with a pretty
straight face, that he had heard of Captain Malyoe and who
he was.

"Well," says Mr. Greenfield, "if Jack Malyoe was a desperate
pirate and a wild, reckless blade twenty years ago, why, he is
Sir John Malyoe now and the owner of a fine estate in Devonshire. Well, Master Barnaby, when one is a baronet and come
into the inheritance of a fine estate (though I do hear it is
vastly cumbered with debts), the world will wink its eye to
much that he may have done twenty years ago. I do hear say,
though, that his own kin still turn the cold shoulder to him."

To this address Barnaby answered nothing, but sat smoking
away at his cigarro at a great rate.

And so that night Barnaby True came face to face for the
first time with the man who murdered his own grandfather—
the greatest beast of a man that ever he met in all of his life.

That time in the harbor he had seen Sir John Malyoe at a
distance and in the darkness; now that he beheld him near by
it seemed to him that he had never looked at a more evil face
in all his life. Not that the man was altogether ugly, for he
had a good nose and a fine double chin; but his eyes stood out
like balls and were red and watery, and he winked them con-

tinually, as though they were always smarting; and his lips were thick and purple-red, and his fat, red cheeks were mottled here and there with little clots of purple veins; and when he spoke his voice rattled so in his throat that it made one wish to clear one's own throat to listen to him. So, what with a pair of fat, white hands, and that hoarse voice, and his swollen face, and his thick lips sticking out, it seemed to Barnaby True he had never seen a countenance so distasteful to him as that one into which he then looked.

But if Sir John Malyoe was so displeasing to our hero's taste, why, the granddaughter, even this first time he beheld her, seemed to him to be the most beautiful, lovely young lady that ever he saw. She had a thin, fair skin, red lips, and yellow hair—though it was then powdered pretty white for the occasion—and the bluest eyes that Barnaby beheld in all of his life. A sweet, timid creature, who seemed not to dare so much as to speak a word for herself without looking to Sir John for leave to do so, and would shrink and shudder whenever he would speak of a sudden to her or direct a sudden glance upon her. When she did speak, it was in so low a voice that one had to bend his head to hear her, and even if she smiled would catch herself and look up as though to see if she had leave to be cheerful.

As for Sir John, he sat at dinner like a pig, and gobbled and ate and drank, smacking his lips all the while, but with hardly a word to either her or Mrs. Greenfield or to Barnaby True; but with a sour, sullen air, as though he would say, "Your damned victuals and drink are no better than they should be, but I must eat 'em or nothing." A great bloated beast of a man!

Only after dinner was over and the young lady and the two misses sat off in a corner together did Barnaby hear her talk

55

with any ease. Then, to be sure, her tongue became loose, and she prattled away at a great rate, though hardly above her breath, until of a sudden her grandfather called out, in his hoarse, rattling voice, that it was time to go. Whereupon she stopped short in what she was saying and jumped up from her chair, looking as frightened as though she had been caught in something amiss, and was to be punished for it.

Barnaby True and Mr. Greenfield both went out to see the two into their coach, where Sir John's man stood holding the lantern. And who should he be, to be sure, but that same lean villain with bald head who had offered to shoot the leader of our hero's expedition out on the harbor that night! For, one of the circles of light from the lantern shining up into his face, Barnaby True knew him the moment he clapped eyes upon him. Though he could not have recognized our hero, he grinned at him in the most impudent, familiar fashion, and never so much as touched his hat either to him or to Mr. Greenfield; but as soon as his master and his young mistress had entered the coach, banged to the door and scrambled up on the seat alongside the driver, and so away without a word, but with another impudent grin, this time favoring both Barnaby and the old gentleman.

Such were these two, master and man, and what Barnaby saw of them then was only confirmed by further observation— the most hateful couple he ever knew; though, God knows, what they afterward suffered should wipe out all complaint against them.

The next day Sir John Malyoe's belongings began to come aboard the *Belle Helen,* and in the afternoon that same lean, villainous manservant comes skipping across the gangplank as nimble as a goat, with two black men behind him lugging a great sea chest. "What!" he cried out, "and so you is the super-cargo, is you? Why, I thought you was more account when

I saw you last night a-sitting talking with His Honor like his equal. Well, no matter; 'tis something to have a brisk, genteel young fellow for a supercargo. So come, my hearty, lend a hand, will you, and help me set His Honor's cabin to rights."

What a speech was this to endure from such a fellow, to be sure! and Barnaby so high in his own esteem, and holding himself a gentleman! Well, what with his distaste for the villain, and what with such odious familiarity, you can guess into what temper so impudent an address must have cast him. "You'll find the steward in yonder," he said, "and he'll show you the cabin," and therewith turned and walked away with prodigious dignity, leaving the other standing where he was.

As he entered his own cabin he could not but see, out of the tail of his eye, that the fellow was still standing where he had left him, regarding him with a most evil, malevolent countenance, so that he had the satisfaction of knowing that he had made one enemy during that voyage who was not very likely to forgive or forget what he must regard as a slight put upon him.

The next day Sir John Malyoe himself came aboard, accompanied by his granddaughter, and followed by this man, and he followed again by four black men, who carried among them two trunks, not large in size, but prodigious heavy in weight, and toward which Sir John and his follower devoted the utmost solicitude and care to see that they were properly carried into the state cabin he was to occupy. Barnaby True was standing in the great cabin as they passed close by him; but though Sir John Malyoe looked hard at him and straight in the face, he never so much as spoke a single word, or showed by a look or a sign that he knew who our hero was. At this the serving man, who saw it all with eyes as quick as a cat's, fell to grinning and chuckling to see Barnaby in his turn so slighted.

The young lady, who also saw it all, flushed up red, then in the instant of passing looked straight at our hero, and bowed and smiled at him with a most sweet and gracious affability, then the next moment recovering herself, as though mightily frightened at what she had done.

The same day the *Belle Helen* sailed, with as beautiful, sweet weather as ever a body could wish for.

There were only two other passengers aboard, the Rev. Simon Styles, the master of a flourishing academy in Spanish Town, and his wife, a good, worthy old couple, but very quiet, and would sit in the great cabin by the hour together reading, so that, what with Sir John Malyoe staying all the time in his own cabin with those two trunks he held so precious, it fell upon Barnaby True in great part to show attention to the young lady; and glad enough he was of the opportunity, as anyone may guess. For when you consider a brisk, lively young man of one-and-twenty and a sweet, beautiful miss of seventeen so thrown together day after day for two weeks, the weather being very fair, as I have said, and the ship tossing and bowling along before a fine humming breeze that sent white caps all over the sea, and with nothing to do but sit and look at that blue sea and the bright sky overhead, it is not hard to suppose what was to befall, and what pleasure it was to Barnaby True to show attention to her.

But, oh! those days when a man is young, and, whether wisely or no, fallen in love! How often during that voyage did our hero lie awake in his berth at night, tossing this way and that without sleep—not that he wanted to sleep if he could, but would rather lie so awake thinking about her and staring into the darkness!

Poor fool! He might have known that the end must come to such a fool's paradise before very long. For who was he to look up to Sir John Malyoe's granddaughter, he, the supercargo of a merchant ship, and she the granddaughter of a baronet.

Nevertheless, things went along very smooth and pleasant, until one evening, when all came of a sudden to an end. At that time he and the young lady had been standing for a long while together, leaning over the rail and looking out across the water through the dusk toward the westward, where the sky was still of a lingering brightness. She had been mightily quiet and dull all that evening, but now of a sudden she began, without any preface whatever, to tell Barnaby about herself and her affairs. She said that she and her grandfather were going to New York that they might take passage thence to Boston town, there to meet her cousin Captain Malyoe, who was stationed in garrison at that place. Then she went on to say that Captain Malyoe was the next heir to the Devonshire estate, and that she and he were to be married in the fall.

But, poor Barnaby! what a fool was he, to be sure! Methinks when she first began to speak about Captain Malyoe he knew what was coming. But now that she had told him, he could say nothing, but stood there staring across the ocean, his breath coming hot and dry as ashes in his throat. She, poor thing, went on to say, in a very low voice, that she had liked him from the very first moment she had seen him, and had been very happy for these days, and would always think of him as a dear friend who had been very kind to her, who had so little pleasure in life, and so would always remember him.

Then they were both silent, until at last Barnaby made shift to say, though in a hoarse and croaking voice, that Captain Malyoe must be a very happy man, and that if he were in Captain Malyoe's place he would be the happiest man in the world. Thus, having spoken, and so found his tongue, he went on to tell her, with his head all in a whirl, that he, too, loved her, and that what she had told him struck him to the heart, and made him the most miserable, unhappy wretch in the whole world.

59

She was not angry at what he said, nor did she turn to look at him, but only said, in a low voice, he should not talk so, for that it could only be a pain to them both to speak of such things, and that whether she would or no, she must do everything as her grandfather bade her, for that he was indeed a terrible man.

To this poor Barnaby could only repeat that he loved her with all his heart, that he had hoped for nothing in his love, but that he was now the most miserable man in the world.

It was at this moment, so tragic for him, that some one who had been hiding nigh them all the while suddenly moved away, and Barnaby True could see in the gathering darkness that it was that villain manservant of Sir John Malyoe's and knew that he must have overheard all that had been said.

The man went straight to the great cabin, and poor Barnaby, his brain all atingle, stood looking after him, feeling that now indeed the last drop of bitterness had been added to his trouble to have such a wretch overhear what he had said.

The young lady could not have seen the fellow, for she continued leaning over the rail, and Barnaby True, standing at her side, not moving, but in such a tumult of many passions that he was like one bewildered, and his heart beating as though to smother him.

So they stood for I know not how long when, of a sudden, Sir John Malyoe comes running out of the cabin, without his hat, but carrying his gold-headed cane, and so straight across the deck to where Barnaby and the young lady stood, that spying wretch close at his heels, grinning like an imp.

"You hussy!" bawled out Sir John, so soon as he had come pretty near them, and in so loud a voice that all on deck might have heard the words; and as he spoke he waved his cane back and forth as though he would have struck the young lady, who, shrinking back almost upon the deck, crouched as though to

60

escape such a blow. "You hussy!" he bawled out with vile oaths, too horrible here to be set down. "What do you do here with this Yankee supercargo, not fit for a gentlewoman to wipe her feet upon? Get to your cabin, you hussy" (only it was something worse he called her this time), "before I lay this cane across your shoulders!"

What with the whirling of Barnaby's brains and the passion into which he was already melted, what with his despair and his love, and his anger at this address, a man gone mad could scarcely be less accountable for his actions than was he at that moment. Hardly knowing what he did, he put his hand against Sir John Malyoe's breast and thrust him violently back, crying out upon him in a great, loud, hoarse voice for threatening a young lady, and saying that for a farthing he would wrench the stick out of his hand and throw it overboard.

Sir John went staggering back with the push Barnaby gave him, and then caught himself up again. Then, with a great bellow, ran roaring at our hero, whirling his cane about, and I do believe would have struck him (and God knows then what might have happened) had not his manservant caught him and held him back.

"Keep back!" cried out our hero, still mighty hoarse. "Keep back! If you strike me with that stick I'll fling you overboard!"

By this time, what with the sound of loud voices and the stamping of feet, some of the crew and others aboard were hurrying up, and the next moment Captain Manly and the first mate, Mr. Freesden, came running out of the cabin. But Barnaby, who was by this fairly set agoing, could not now stop himself.

"And who are you, anyhow," he cried out, "to threaten to strike me and to insult me, who am as good as you? You dare not strike me! You may shoot a man from behind, as you shot poor Captain Brand on the Rio Cobra River, but you won't dare strike me face to face. I know who you are and what you are!"

By this time Sir John Malyoe had ceased to endeavor to strike him, but stood stock-still, his great bulging eyes staring as though they would pop out of his head.

"What's all this?" cries Captain Manly, bustling up to them with Mr. Freesden. "What does all this mean?"

But, as I have said, our hero was too far gone now to contain himself until all that he had to say was out.

"The damned villain insulted me and insulted the young lady," he cried out, panting in the extremity of his passion, "and then he threatened to strike me with his cane. But I know who he is and what he is. I know what he's got in his cabin in those two trunks, and where he found it, and whom it belongs to. He found it on the shores of the Rio Cobra River, and I have only to open my mouth and tell what I know about it."

At this Captain Manly clapped his hand upon our hero's shoulder and fell to shaking him so that he could scarcely stand, calling out to him the while to be silent. "What do you mean?" he cried. "An officer of this ship to quarrel with a passenger of mine! Go straight to your cabin, and stay there till I give you leave to come out again."

At this Master Barnaby came somewhat back to himself and into his wits again with a jump. "But he threatened to strike me with his cane, Captain," he cried out, "and that I won't stand from any man!"

"No matter what he did," said Captain Manly, very sternly. "Go to your cabin, as I bid you, and stay there till I tell you to come out again, and when we get to New York I'll take pains to tell your stepfather of how you have behaved. I'll have no such rioting as this aboard my ship."

Barnaby True looked around him, but the young lady was

gone. Nor, in the blindness of his frenzy, had he seen when she had gone nor whither she went. As for Sir John Malyoe, he stood in the light of a lantern, his face gone as white as ashes, and I do believe if a look could kill, the dreadful malevolent stare he fixed upon Barnaby True would have slain him where he stood.

After Captain Manly had so shaken some wits into poor Barnaby he, unhappy wretch, went to his cabin, as he was bidden to do, and there, shutting the door upon himself, and flinging himself down, all dressed as he was, upon his berth, yielded himself over to the profoundest passion of humiliation and despair.

There he lay for I know not how long, staring into the darkness, until by and by, in spite of his suffering and his despair, he dozed off into a loose sleep, that was more like waking than sleep, being possessed continually by the most vivid and distasteful dreams, from which he would awaken only to doze off and to dream again.

It was from the midst of one of these extravagant dreams that he was suddenly aroused by the noise of a pistol shot, and then the noise of another and another, and then a great bump and a grinding jar, and then the sound of many footsteps running across the deck and down into the great cabin. Then came a tremendous uproar of voices in the great cabin, the struggling as of men's bodies being tossed about, striking violently against the partitions and bulkheads. At the same instant arose a screaming of women's voices, and one voice, and that Sir John Malyoe's, crying out as in the greatest extremity: "You villains! You damned villains!" and with the sudden detonation of a pistol fired into the close space of the great cabin.

Barnaby was out in the middle of his cabin in a moment,

and taking only time enough to snatch down one of the pistols that hung at the head of his berth, flung out into the great cabin, to find it as black as night, the lantern slung there having been either blown out or dashed out into darkness. The prodigiously dark space was full of uproar, the hubbub and confusion pierced through and through by that keen sound of women's voices screaming, one in the cabin and the other in the stateroom beyond. Almost immediately Barnaby pitched headlong over two or three struggling men scuffling together upon the deck, falling with a great clatter and the loss of his pistol, which, however, he regained almost immediately.

What all the uproar meant he could not tell, but he presently heard Captain Manly's voice from somewhere suddenly calling out, "You bloody pirate, would you choke me to death?" wherewith some notion of what had happened came to him like a flash, and that they had been attacked in the night by pirates.

Looking toward the companionway, he saw, outlined against the darkness of the night without, the blacker form of a man's figure, standing still and motionless as a statue in the midst of all this hubbub, and so by some instinct he knew in a moment that that must be the master maker of all this devil's brew. Therewith, still kneeling upon the deck, he covered the bosom of that shadowy figure pointblank, as he thought, with his pistol, and instantly pulled the trigger.

In the flash of red light, and in the instant stunning report of the pistol shot, Barnaby saw, as stamped upon the blackness, a broad, flat face with fishy eyes, a lean, bony forehead with what appeared to be a great blotch of blood upon the side, a cocked hat trimmed with gold lace, a red scarf across the breast, and the gleam of brass buttons. Then the darkness, very thick and black, swallowed everything again.

But in the instant Sir John Malyoe called out, in a great loud voice: "My God! 'Tis William Brand!" Therewith came the sound of some one falling heavily down.

The next moment, Barnaby's sight coming back to him again in the darkness, he beheld that dark and motionless figure still standing exactly where it had stood before, and so knew either that he had missed it or else that it was of so supernatural a sort that a leaden bullet might do it no harm. Though if it was indeed an apparition that Barnaby beheld in that moment, there is this to say, that he saw it as plain as ever he saw a living man in all of his life.

This was the last our hero knew, for the next moment somebody—whether by accident or design he never knew—struck him such a terrible violent blow upon the side of the head that he saw forty thousand stars flash before his eyeballs, and then, with a great humming in his head, swooned dead away.

When Barnaby True came back to his senses again it was to find himself being cared for with great skill and nicety, his head bathed with cold water, and a bandage being bound about it as carefully as though a chirurgeon was attending to him.

He could not immediately recall what had happened to him, nor until he had opened his eyes to find himself in a strange cabin, extremely well fitted and painted with white and gold, the light of a lantern shining in his eyes, together with the gray of the early daylight through the dead-eye. Two men were bending over him—one, a negro in a striped shirt, with a yellow handkerchief around his head and silver earrings in his ears; the other, a white man, clad in a strange outlandish dress of a foreign make, and with great mustachios hanging down, and with gold earrings in his ears.

It was the latter who was attending to Barnaby's hurt with such extreme care and gentleness.

65

All this Barnaby saw with his first clear consciousness after his swoon. Then remembering what had befallen him, and his head beating as though it would split asunder, he shut his eyes again, contriving with great effort to keep himself from groaning aloud, and wondering as to what sort of pirates these could be who would first knock a man in the head so terrible a blow as that which he had suffered, and then take such care to fetch him back to life again, and to make him easy and comfortable.

Nor did he open his eyes again, but lay there gathering his wits together and wondering thus until the bandage was properly tied about his head and sewed together. Then once more he opened his eyes, and looked up to ask where he was.

Either they who were attending to him did not choose to reply, or else they could not speak English, for they made no answer, excepting by signs; for the white man, seeing that he was now able to speak, and so was come back into his senses again, nodded his head three or four times, and smiled with a grin of his white teeth, and then pointed, as though toward a saloon beyond. At the same time the negro held up our hero's coat and beckoned for him to put it on, so that Barnaby, seeing that it was required of him to meet some one without, arose, though with a good deal of effort, and permitted the negro to help him on with his coat, still feeling mightily dizzy and uncertain upon his legs, his head beating fit to split, and the vessel rolling and pitching at a great rate, as though upon a heavy ground swell.

So, still sick and dizzy, he went out into what was indeed a fine saloon beyond, painted in white and gilt like the cabin he had just quitted, and fitted in the nicest fashion, a mahogany table, polished very bright, extending the length of the room, and a quantity of bottles, together with glasses of clear crystal, arranged in a hanging rack above.

Here at the table a man was sitting with his back to our hero, clad in a rough pea-jacket, and with a red handkerchief tied around his throat, his feet stretched out before him, and he smoking a pipe of tobacco with all the ease and comfort in the world.

As Barnaby came in he turned round, and, to the profound astonishment of our hero, presented toward him in the light of the lantern, the dawn shining pretty strong through the skylight, the face of that very man who had conducted the mysterious expedition that night across Kingston Harbor to the Rio Cobra River.

This man looked steadily at Barnaby True for a moment or two, and then burst out laughing; and, indeed, Barnaby, standing there with the bandage about his head, must have looked a very droll picture of that astonishment he felt so profoundly at finding who was this pirate into whose hands he had fallen.

"Well," says the other, "and so you be up at last, and no great harm done, I'll be bound. And how does your head feel by now, my young master?"

To this Barnaby made no reply, but, what with wonder and the dizziness of his head, seated himself at the table over against the speaker, who pushed a bottle of rum toward him, together with a glass from the swinging shelf above.

He watched Barnaby fill his glass, and so soon as he had done so began immediately by saying: "I do suppose you think you were treated mightily ill to be so handled last night. Well, so you were treated ill enough—though who hit you that crack upon the head I know no more than a child unborn. Well, I am sorry for the way you were handled, but there is this much to say, and of that you may believe me, that nothing was meant to you but kindness, and before you are through with us all you will believe that well enough."

Here he helped himself to a taste of grog, and sucking in his lips, went on again with what he had to say. "Do you remember," said he, "that expedition of ours in Kingston Harbor, and how we were all of us balked that night?"

"Why, yes," said Barnaby True, "nor am I likely to forget it."

"And do you remember what I said to that villain, Jack Malyoe, that night as his boat went by us?"

"As to that," said Barnaby True, "I do not know that I can say yes or no, but if you will tell me, I will maybe answer you in kind."

"Why, I mean this," said the other. "I said that the villain had got the better of us once again, but that next time it would be our turn, even if William Brand himself had to come back from hell to put the business through."

"I remember something of the sort," said Barnaby, "now that you speak of it, but still I am all in the dark as to what you are driving at."

The other looked at him very cunningly for a little while, his head on one side, and his eyes half shut. Then, as if satisfied, he suddenly burst out laughing. "Look hither," said he, "and I'll show you something," and therewith, moving to one side, disclosed a couple of traveling cases or small trunks with brass studs, so exactly like those that Sir John Malyoe had fetched aboard at Jamaica that Barnaby, putting this and that together, knew that they must be the same.

Our hero had a strong enough suspicion as to what those two cases contained, and his suspicions had become a certainty when he saw Sir John Malyoe struck all white at being threatened about them, and his face lowering so malevolently as to look murder had he dared do it. But, Lord! what were suspicions or even certainty to what Barnaby True's two eyes beheld when that man lifted the lids of the two cases—the locks thereof having already been forced—and, flinging back

first one lid and then the other, displayed to Barnaby's astonished sight a great treasure of gold and silver! Most of it tied
up in leathern bags, to be sure, but many of the coins, big and
little, yellow and white, lying loose and scattered about like
so many beans, brimming the cases to the very top.

Barnaby sat dumb-struck at what he beheld; as to whether
he breathed or no, I cannot tell; but this I know, that he sat
staring at that marvelous treasure like a man in a trance, until,
after a few seconds of this golden display, the other banged
down the lids again and burst out laughing whereupon he came
back to himself with a jump.

"Well, and what do you think of that?" said the other. "Is
it not enough for a man to turn pirate for? But," he continued,
"it is not for the sake of showing you this that I have been
waiting for you here so long a while, but to tell you that you
are not the only passenger aboard, but that there is another,
whom I am to confide to your care and attention, according to
orders I have received; so, if you are ready, Master Barnaby,
I'll fetch her in directly." He waited for a moment, as though
for Barnaby to speak, but our hero not replying, he arose and,
putting away the bottle of rum and the glasses, crossed the
saloon to a door like that from which Barnaby had come a little
while before. This he opened, and after a moment's delay and
a few words spoken to some one within, ushered thence a
young lady, who came out very slowly into the saloon where
Barnaby still sat at the table.

It was Miss Marjorie Malyoe, very white, and looking as
though stunned or bewildered by all that had befallen her.

Barnaby True could never tell whether the amazing strange
voyage that followed was of long or of short duration; whether
it occupied three days or ten days. For conceive, if you choose,
two people of flesh and blood moving and living continually in
all the circumstances and surroundings as of a nightmare

dream, yet they two so happy together that all the universe beside was of no moment to them! How was anyone to tell whether in such circumstances any time appeared to be long or short? Does a dream appear to be long or to be short?

The vessel in which they sailed was a brigantine of good size and build, but manned by a considerable crew, the most strange and outlandish in their appearance that Barnaby had ever beheld—some white, some yellow, some black, and all tricked out with gay colors, and gold earrings in their ears, and some with great long mustachios, and others with handker-chiefs tied around their heads, and all talking a language to-gether of which Barnaby True could understand not a single word, but which might have been Portuguese from one or two phrases he caught. Nor did this strange, mysterious crew, of God knows what sort of men, seem to pay any attention what-ever to Barnaby or to the young lady. They might now and then have looked at him and her out of the corners of their yellow eyes, but that was all; otherwise they were indeed like the creatures of a nightmare dream. Only he who was the captain of this outlandish crew would maybe speak to Barnaby a few words as to the weather or what not when he would come down into the saloon to mix a glass of grog or to light a pipe of tobacco, and then to go on deck again about his busi-ness. Otherwise our hero and the young lady were left to themselves, to do as they pleased, with no one to interfere with them.

As for her, she at no time showed any great sign of terror or of fear, only for a little while was singularly numb and quiet, as though dazed with what had happened to her. Indeed, methinks that wild beast, her grandfather, had so crushed her spirit by his tyranny and his violence that nothing that hap-pened to her might seem sharp and keen, as it does to others of an ordinary sort.

But this was only at first, for afterward her face began to grow singularly clear, as with a white light, and she would sit quite still, permitting Barnaby to gaze, I know not how long, into her eyes, her face so transfigured and her lips smiling, and they, as it were, neither of them breathing, but hearing, as in another far-distant place, the outlandish jargon of the crew talking together in the warm, bright sunlight, or the sound of creaking block and tackle as they hauled upon the sheets.

Is it, then, any wonder that Barnaby True could never remember whether such a voyage as this was long or short?

It was as though they might have sailed so upon that wonderful voyage forever. You may guess how amazed was Barnaby True when, coming upon deck one morning, he found the brigantine riding upon an even keel, at anchor off Staten Island, a small village on the shore, and the well-known roofs and chimneys of New York town in plain sight across the water.

'Twas the last place in the world he had expected to see.

And, indeed, it did seem strange to lie there alongside Staten Island all that day, with New York town so nigh at hand and yet so impossible to reach. For whether he desired to escape or no, Barnaby True could not but observe that both he and the young lady were so closely watched that they might as well have been prisoners, tied hand and foot and laid in the hold, so far as any hope of getting away was concerned.

All that day there was a deal of mysterious coming and going aboard the brigantine, and in the afternoon a sailboat went up to the town, carrying the captain, and a great load covered over with a tarpaulin in the stern. What was so taken up to the town Barnaby did not then guess, but the boat did not return again till about sundown.

For the sun was just dropping below the water when the captain came aboard once more and, finding Barnaby on deck, bade him come down into the saloon, where they found the

71

young lady sitting, the broad light of the evening shining in through the skylight, and making it all pretty bright within.

The captain commanded Barnaby to be seated, for he had something of moment to say to him; whereupon, as soon as Barnaby had taken his place alongside the young lady, he began very seriously, with a preface somewhat thus: "Though you may think me the captain of this brigantine, young gentlemen, I am not really so, but am under orders, and so have only carried out those orders of a superior in all these things that I have done." Having so begun, he went on to say that there was one thing yet remaining for him to do, and that the greatest thing of all. He said that Barnaby and the young lady had not been fetched away from the *Belle Helen* as they were by any mere chance of accident, but that 'twas all a plan laid by a head wiser than his, and carried out by one whom he must obey in all things. He said that he hoped that both Barnaby and the young lady would perform willingly what they would be now called upon to do, but that whether they did it willingly or no, they must, for that those were the orders of one who was not to be disobeyed.

You may guess how our hero held his breath at all this; but whatever might have been his expectations, the very wildest of them all did not reach to that which was demanded of him. "My orders are these," said the other, continuing: "I am to take you and the young lady ashore, and to see that you are married before I quit you; and to that end a very good, decent, honest minister who lives ashore yonder in the village was chosen and hath been spoken to and is now, no doubt, waiting for you to come. Such are my orders, and this is the last thing I am set to do; so now I will leave you alone together for five minutes to talk it over, but be quick about it, for whether willing or not, this thing must be done."

Thereupon he went away, as he had promised, leaving those

72

two alone together, Barnaby like one turned into stone, and the young lady, her face turned away, flaming as red as fire in the fading light.

Nor can I tell what Barnaby said to her, nor what words he used, but only, all in a tumult, with neither beginning nor end he told her that God knew he loved her, and that with all his heart and soul, and that there was nothing in all the world for him but her; but, nevertheless, if she would not have it as had been ordered, and if she were not willing to marry him as she was bidden to do, he would rather die than lend himself to forcing her to do such a thing against her will. Nevertheless, he told her she must speak up and tell him yes or no, and that God knew he would give all the world if she would say "yes."

All this and more he said in such a tumult of words that there was no order in their speaking, and she sitting there, her bosom rising and falling as though her breath stifled her. Nor may I tell what she replied to him, only this, that she said she would marry him. At this he took her into his arms and set his lips to hers, his heart all melting away in his bosom.

So presently came the captain back into the saloon again, to find Barnaby sitting there holding her hand, she with her face turned away, and his heart beating like a trip hammer, and so saw that all was settled as he would have it. Wherewith he wished them both joy, and gave Barnaby his hand.

The yawlboat belonging to the brigantine was ready and waiting alongside when they came upon deck, and immediately they descended to it and took their seats. So they landed, and in a little while were walking up the village street in the darkness, she clinging to his arm as though she would swoon, and the captain of the brigantine and two other men from aboard following after them. And so to the minister's house, finding him waiting for them, smoking his pipe in the warm evening, and walking up and down in front of his own door. He immediately conducted them into the house, where, his wife having fetched a candle, and two others of the village folk being present, the good man having asked several questions as to their names and their age and where they were from, the ceremony was performed, and the certificate duly signed by those present—excepting the men who had come ashore from the brigantine, and who refused to set their hands to any paper.

The same sailboat that had taken the captain up to the town in the afternoon was waiting for them at the landing place, whence, the captain, having wished them Godspeed, and having shaken Barnaby very heartily by the hand, they pushed off, and, coming about, ran away with the slant of the wind, dropping the shore and those strange beings alike behind them into the night.

As they sped away through the darkness they could hear the creaking of the sails being hoisted aboard of the brigantine, and so knew that she was about to put to sea once more. Nor did Barnaby True ever set eyes upon those beings again, nor did anyone else that I ever heard tell of.

It was nigh midnight when they made Mr. Hartright's wharf at the foot of Wall Street, and so the streets were all dark and silent and deserted as they walked up to Barnaby's home.

You may conceive of the wonder and amazement of Barnaby's dear stepfather when, clad in a dressing gown and carrying a lighted candle in his hand, he unlocked and unbarred the door, and so saw who it was had aroused him at such an hour of the night, and the young and beautiful lady whom Barnaby had fetched with him.

The first thought of the good man was that the *Belle Helen* had come into port; nor did Barnaby undeceive him as he led the way into the house, but waited until they were all safe and sound in privity together before he should unfold his strange and wonderful story.

74

"This was left for you by two foreign sailors this afternoon, Barnaby," the good old man said, as he led the way through the hall, holding up the candle at the same time, so that Barnaby might see an object that stood against the wainscoting by the door of the dining room.

Nor could Barnaby refrain from crying out with amazement when he saw that it was one of the two chests of treasure that Sir John Malyoe had fetched from Jamaica, and which the pirates had taken from the *Belle Helen*. As for Mr. Hartright, he guessed no more what was in it than the man in the moon.

The next day but one brought the *Belle Helen* herself into port, with the terrible news not only of having been attacked at night by pirates, but also that Sir John Malyoe was dead. For whether it was the sudden shock of the sight of his old captain's face—whom he himself had murdered and thought dead and buried—flashing so out against the darkness, or whether it was the strain of passion that overset his brains, certain it is that when the pirates left the *Belle Helen,* carrying with them the young lady and Barnaby and the traveling trunks, those left aboard the *Belle Helen* found Sir John Malyoe lying in a fit upon the floor, frothing at the mouth and black in the face, as though he had been choked, and so took him away to his berth, where, the next morning about ten o'clock, he died, without once having opened his eyes or spoken a single word.

As for the villain manservant, no one ever saw him afterward; though whether he jumped overboard, or whether the pirates who so attacked the ship had carried him away bodily, who shall say?

Mr. Hartright, after he had heard Barnaby's story, had been very uncertain as to the ownership of the chest of treasure that had been left by those men for Barnaby, but the news of the death of Sir John Malyoe made the matter very easy for him to decide. For surely if that treasure did not belong to Barnaby, there could be no doubt that it must belong to his wife, she being Sir John Malyoe's legal heir. And so it was that that great fortune (in actual computation amounting to upward of sixty-three thousand pounds) came to Barnaby True, the grandson of that famous pirate, William Brand; the English estate in Devonshire, in default of male issue of Sir John Malyoe, descended to Captain Malyoe, whom the young lady was to have married.

As for the other case of treasure, it was never heard of again, nor could Barnaby ever guess whether it was divided as booty among the pirates, or whether they had carried it away with them to some strange and foreign land, there to share it among themselves.

And so the ending of the story, with only this to observe, that whether that strange appearance of Captain Brand's face by the light of the pistol was a ghostly and spiritual appearance, or whether he was present in flesh and blood, there is only to say that he was never heard of again; nor had he ever been heard of till that time since the day he was so shot from behind by Capt. John Malyoe on the banks of the Rio Cobra River in the year 1733.

III

WITH THE BUCCANEERS

*Being an Account of Certain Adventures that
Befell Henry Mostyn Under Capt. H. Morgan
in the Year 1665–66*

1

LTHOUGH this narration has more particularly to do with the taking of the Spanish vice admiral in the harbor of Porto Bello, and of the rescue therefrom of Le Sieur Simon, his wife and daughter (the adventure of which was successfully achieved by Captain Morgan, the famous buccaneer), we shall, nevertheless, premise something of the earlier history of Master Harry Mostyn, whom you may, if you please, consider as the hero of the several circumstances recounted in these pages.

In the year 1664 our hero's father embarked from Portsmouth, in England, for the Barbados, where he owned a considerable sugar plantation. Thither to those parts of America he transported with himself his whole family, of whom our

Master Harry was the fifth of eight children—a great lusty fellow as little fitted for the Church (for which he was designed) as could be. At the time of this story, though not above sixteen years old, Master Harry Mostyn was as big and well-grown as many a man of twenty, and of such a reckless and dare-devil spirit that no adventure was too dangerous or too mischievous for him to embark upon.

At this time there was a deal of talk in those parts of the Americas concerning Captain Morgan, and the prodigious successes he was having pirating against the Spaniards.

This man had once been an indentured servant with Mr. Rolls, a sugar factor at the Barbados. Having served out his time, and being of lawless disposition, possessing also a prodigious appetite for adventure, he joined with others of his kidney, and purchasing a caravel of three guns, embarked fairly upon that career of piracy the most successful that ever was heard of in the world.

Master Harry had known this man very well while he was still with Mr. Rolls, serving as a clerk at that gentleman's sugar wharf, a tall, broad-shouldered, strapping fellow, with red cheeks, and thick red lips, and rolling blue eyes, and hair as red as any chestnut. Many knew him for a bold, gruff-spoken man, but no one at that time suspected that he had it in him to become so famous and renowned as he afterward grew to be.

The fame of his exploits had been the talk of those parts for above a twelvemonth, when, in the latter part of the year 1665, Captain Morgan, having made a very successful expedition against the Spaniards into the Gulf of Campeche—where he took several important purchases from the plate fleet —came to the Barbados, there to fit out another such venture, and to enlist recruits.

He and certain other adventurers had purchased a vessel of some five hundred tons, which they proposed to convert into a

The Buccaneer Was a Picturesque Fellow

pirate by cutting portholes for cannon, and running three or four carronades across her main deck. The name of this ship, be it mentioned, was the *Good Samaritan,* as ill-fitting a name as could be for such a craft, which, instead of being designed for the healing of wounds, was intended to inflict such devastation as those wicked men proposed.

Here was a piece of mischief exactly fitted to our hero's tastes; wherefore, having made up a bundle of clothes, and with not above a shilling in his pocket, he made an excursion into the town to seek for Captain Morgan. There he found the great pirate established at an ordinary, with a little court of ragamuffins and swashbucklers gathered about him, all talking very loud, and drinking healths in raw rum as though it were sugared water.

And what a fine figure our buccaneer had grown, to be sure! How different from the poor, humble clerk upon the sugar wharf! What a deal of gold braid! What a fine, silver-hilted Spanish sword! What a gay velvet sling, hung with three silver-mounted pistols! If Master Harry's mind had not been made up before, to be sure such a spectacle of glory would have determined it.

This figure of war our hero asked to step aside with him, and when they had come into a corner, proposed to the other what he intended, and that he had a mind to enlist as a gentle-man adventurer upon this expedition. Upon this our rogue of a buccaneer captain burst out a-laughing, and fetching Master Harry a great thump upon the back, swore roundly that he would make a man of him, and that it was a pity to make a parson out of so good a piece of stuff.

Nor was Captain Morgan less good than his word, for when the *Good Samaritan* set sail with a favoring wind for the island of Jamaica, Master Harry found himself established as one of the adventurers aboard.

79

2

Could you but have seen the town of Port Royal as it appeared in the year 1665 you would have beheld a sight very well worth while looking upon. There were no fine houses at that time, and no great counting houses built of brick, such as you may find nowadays, but a crowd of board and wattled huts huddled along the streets, and all so gay with flags and bits of color that Vanity Fair itself could not have been gayer. To this place came all the pirates and buccaneers that infested those parts, and men shouted and swore and gambled, and poured out money like water, and then maybe wound up their merrymaking by dying of fever. For the sky in these torrid latitudes is all full of clouds overhead, and as hot as any blanket, and when the sun shone forth it streamed down upon the smoking sands so that the houses were ovens and the streets were furnaces; so it was little wonder that men died like rats in a hole. But little they appeared to care for that; so that everywhere you might behold a multitude of painted women and Jews and merchants and pirates, gaudy with red scarfs and gold braid and all sorts of odds and ends of foolish finery, all fighting and gambling and bartering for that ill-gotten treasure of the berobbed Spaniard.

Here, arriving, Captain Morgan found a hearty welcome, and a message from the governor awaiting him, the message bidding him attend His Excellency upon the earliest occasion that offered. Whereupon, taking our hero (of whom he had grown prodigiously fond) along with him, our pirate went, without any loss of time, to visit Sir Thomas Modiford, who was then the royal governor of all this devil's brew of wickedness.

They found His Excellency seated in a great easy-chair, under the shadow of a slatted veranda, the floor whereof was paved with brick. He was clad, for the sake of coolness, only in his shirt, breeches, and stockings, and he wore slippers on his feet. He was smoking a great cigarro of tobacco, and a goblet of lime juice and water and rum stood at his elbow on a table. Here, out of the glare of the heat, it was all very cool and pleasant, with a sea breeze blowing violently in through the slats, setting them a-rattling now and then, and stirring Sir Thomas's long hair, which he had pushed back for the sake of coolness.

The purport of this interview, I may tell you, concerned the rescue of one Le Sieur Simon, who, together with his wife and daughter, was held captive by the Spaniards.

This gentleman adventurer (Le Sieur Simon) had, a few

years before, been set up by the buccaneers as governor of the
island of Santa Catharina. This place, though well fortified by
the Spaniards, the buccaneers had seized upon, establishing
themselves thereon, and so infesting the commerce of those
seas that no Spanish fleet was safe from them. At last the
Spaniards, no longer able to endure these assaults against their
commerce, sent a great force against the freebooters to drive
them out of their island stronghold. This they did, retaking
Santa Catharina, together with its governor, his wife, and
daughter, as well as the whole garrison of buccaneers.

This garrison was sent by their conquerors, some to the
galleys, some to the mines, some to no man knows where. The
governor himself—Le Sieur Simon—was to be sent to Spain,
there to stand his trial for piracy.

The news of all this, I may tell you, had only just been received in Jamaica, having been brought thither by a Spanish
captain, one Don Roderiguez Sylvia, who was, besides, the
bearer of dispatches to the Spanish authorities relating the
whole affair.

Such, in fine, was the purport of this interview, and as our
hero and his captain walked back together from the governor's
house to the ordinary where they had taken up their inn, the
buccaneer assured his companion that he purposed to obtain
those dispatches from the Spanish captain that very afternoon,
even if he had to use force to seize them.

All this, you are to understand, was undertaken only because
of the friendship that the governor and Captain Morgan entertained for Le Sieur Simon. And, indeed, it was wonderful how
honest and how faithful were these wicked men in their
dealings with one another. For you must know that Governor
Modiford and Le Sieur Simon and the buccaneers were all of
one kidney—all taking a share in the piracies of those times,

and all holding by one another as though they were the honestest men in the world. Hence it was they were also determined to rescue Le Sieur Simon from the Spaniards.

3

Having reached his ordinary after his interview with the governor, Captain Morgan found there a number of his companions, such as usually gathered at that place to be in attendance upon him—some, those belonging to the *Good Samaritan;* others, those who hoped to obtain benefits from him; others, those ragamuffins who gathered around him because he was famous, and because it pleased them to be of his court and to be called his followers. For nearly always your successful pirate had such a little court surrounding him.

Finding a dozen or more of these rascals gathered there, Captain Morgan informed them of his present purpose—that he was going to find the Spanish captain to demand his papers of him, and calling upon them to accompany him.

With this following at his heels, our buccaneer started off down the street, his lieutenant, a Cornishman named Bartholomew Davis, upon one hand and our hero upon the other. So they paraded the streets for the best part of an hour before they found the Spanish captain. For whether he had got wind that Captain Morgan was searching for him, or whether, finding himself in a place so full of his enemies, he had buried himself in some place of hiding, it is certain that the buccaneers had traversed pretty nearly the whole town before they discovered that he was lying at a certain auberge kept by a Portuguese Jew. Thither they went, and thither Captain Morgan entered with the utmost coolnesss and composure of demeanor, his followers crowding noisily in at his heels.

The space within was very dark, being lighted only by the

doorway and by two large slatted windows or openings in the front.

In this dark, hot place—not over-roomy at the best—were gathered twelve or fifteen villainous-appearing men, sitting at tables and drinking together, waited upon by the Jew and his wife. Our hero had no trouble in discovering which of this lot of men was Captain Sylvia, for not only did Captain Morgan direct his glance full of war upon him, but the Spaniard was clad with more particularity and with more show of finery than any of the others who were there.

Him Captain Morgan approached and demanded his papers, whereunto the other replied with such a jabber of Spanish and English that no man could have understood what he said. To this Captain Morgan in turn replied that he must have those papers, no matter what it might cost him to obtain them, and thereupon drew a pistol from his sling and presented it at the other's head.

At this threatening action the innkeeper's wife fell a-screaming, and the Jew, as in a frenzy, besought them not to tear the house down about his ears.

Our hero could hardly tell what followed, only that all of a sudden there was a prodigious uproar of combat. Knives flashed everywhere, and then a pistol was fired so close to his head that he stood like one stunned, hearing some one crying out in a loud voice, but not knowing whether it was a friend or a foe who had been shot. Then another pistol shot so deafened what was left of Master Harry's hearing that his ears rang for above an hour afterward. By this time the whole place was full of gunpowder smoke, and there was the sound of blows and oaths and outcrying and the clashing of knives.

As Master Harry, who had no great stomach for such a combat, and no very particular interest in the quarrel, was making for the door, a little Portuguese, as withered and as nimble as an ape, came ducking under the table and plunged at his stomach with a great long knife, which, had it effected its object, would surely have ended his adventures then and there. Finding himself in such danger, Master Harry snatched up a heavy chair, and, flinging it at his enemy, who was preparing for another attack, he fairly ran for it out of the door, expecting every instant to feel the thrust of the blade betwixt his ribs.

A considerable crowd has gathered outside, and others, hearing the uproar, were coming running to join them. With these our hero stood, trembling like a leaf, and with cold chills running up and down his back like water at the narrow escape from the danger that had threatened him.

Nor shall you think him a coward, for you must remember he was hardly sixteen years old at the time, and that this was the first affair of the sort he had encountered. Afterward, as you shall learn, he showed that he could exhibit courage enough at a pinch.

While he stood there, endeavoring to recover his composure, the while the tumult continued within, suddenly two men came running almost together out of the door, a crowd of the combatants at their heels. The first of these men was Captain Sylvia; the other, who was pursuing him, was Captain Morgan.

As the crowd about the door parted before the sudden appearing of these, the Spanish captain, perceiving, as he supposed, a way of escape opened to him, darted across the street with incredible swiftness toward an alleyway upon the other side. Upon this, seeing his prey like to get away from him, Captain Morgan snatched a pistol out of his sling, and resting it for an instant across his arm, fired at the flying Spaniard, and that with so true an aim that, though the street was now full of people, the other went tumbling over and over all of a heap in the kennel, where he lay, after a twitch or two, as still as a log.

At the sound of the shot and the fall of the man the crowd scattered upon all sides, yelling and screaming, and the street being thus pretty clear, Captain Morgan ran across the way to where his victim lay, his smoking pistol still in his hand, and our hero following close at his heels.

Our poor Harry had never before beheld a man killed thus in an instant who a moment before had been so full of life and activity, for when Captain Morgan turned the body over upon its back he could perceive at a glance, little as he knew of such matters, that the man was stone-dead. And, indeed, it was a dreadful sight for him who was hardly more than a child. He stood rooted for he knew not how long, staring down at the dead face with twitching fingers and shuddering limbs. Meantime a great crowd was gathering about them again. As for Captain Morgan, he went about his work with the utmost coolness and deliberation imaginable, unbuttoning the waistcoat and the shirt of the man he had murdered with fingers that neither twitched nor shook. There were a gold cross and a bunch of silver medals hung by a whipcord about the neck of the dead man. This Captain Morgan broke away with a snap, reaching the jingling baubles to Harry, who took them in his nerveless hand and fingers that he could hardly close upon what they held.

The papers Captain Morgan found in a wallet in an inner breast pocket of the Spaniard's waistcoat. These he examined one by one, and finding them to his satisfaction, tied them up again, and slipped the wallet and its contents into his own pocket.

Then for the first time he appeared to observe Master Harry, who, indeed, must have been standing, the perfect picture of horror and dismay. Whereupon, bursting out a-laughing, and slipping the pistol he had used back into its sling again, he fetched poor Harry a great slap upon the back, bidding him be a man, for that he would see many such sights as this.

But indeed, it was no laughing matter for poor Master Harry, for it was many a day before his imagination could rid itself of the image of the dead Spaniard's face; and as he walked away down the street with his companions, leaving the crowd behind them, and the dead body where it lay for its friends to look after, his ears humming and ringing from the deafening noise of the pistol shots fired in the close room, and the sweat trickling down his face in drops, he knew not whether all that had passed had been real, or whether it was a dream from which he might presently awaken.

4

The papers Captain Morgan had thus seized upon as the fruit of the murder he had committed must have been as perfectly satisfactory to him as could be, for having paid a second visit that evening to Governor Modiford, the pirate lifted anchor the next morning and made sail toward the Gulf of Darien. There, after cruising about in those waters for about a fortnight without falling in with a vessel of any sort, at the end of that time they overhauled a caravel bound from Porto Bello to Cartagena, which vessel they took, and finding her loaded with nothing better than raw hides, scuttled and sank her, being then about twenty leagues from the main of Cartagena. From the captain of this vessel they learned that the plate fleet was then lying in the harbor of Porto Bello, not yet having set sail thence, but waiting for the change of the winds before embarking for Spain. Besides this, which was a good deal more to their purpose, the Spaniards told the pirates that the Sieur Simon, his wife, and daughter were confined aboard the vice admiral of that fleet, and that the name of the vice admiral was the *Santa Maria y Valladolid*.

So soon as Captain Morgan had obtained the information he desired he directed his course straight for the Bay of Santo Blaso, where he might lie safely within the cape of that name without any danger of discovery (that part of the mainland being entirely uninhabited) and yet be within twenty or twenty-five leagues of Porto Bello.

Having come safely to this anchorage, he at once declared his intentions to his companions, which were as follows:

That it was entirely impossible for them to hope to sail their vessel into the harbor of Porto Bello, and to attack the Spanish vice admiral where he lay in the midst of the armed flota; wherefore, if anything was to be accomplished, it must be undertaken by some subtle design rather than by open-handed boldness. Having so prefaced what he had to say, he now declared that it was his purpose to take one of the ship's boats and to go in that to Porto Bello, trusting for some opportunity to occur to aid him either in the accomplishment of his aims or in the gaining of some further information. Having thus delivered himself, he invited any who dared to do so to volunteer for the expedition, telling them plainly that he would constrain no man to go against his will, for that at best it was a desperate enterprise, possessing only the recommendation that in its achievement the few who undertook it would gain great renown, and perhaps a very considerable booty.

And such was the incredible influence of this bold man over his companions, and such was their confidence in his skill and cunning, that not above a dozen of all those aboard hung back from the undertaking, but nearly every man desired to be taken.

Of these volunteers Captain Morgan chose twenty—among

others our Master Harry—and having arranged with his lieutenant that if nothing was heard from the expedition at the
end of three days he should sail for Jamaica to await news, he
embarked upon that enterprise, which, though never hereto-
fore published, was perhaps the boldest and the most desperate
of all those that have since made his name so famous. For
what could be a more unparalleled undertaking than for a little
open boat, containing but twenty men, to enter the harbor of
the third strongest fortress of the Spanish mainland with the
intention of cutting out the Spanish vice admiral from the
midst of a whole fleet of powerfully armed vessels, and how
many men in all the world do you suppose would venture such
a thing?

But there is this to be said of that great buccaneer: that if
he undertook enterprises so desperate as this, he yet laid his
plans so well that they never went altogether amiss. Moreover,
the very desperation of his successes was of such a nature that
no man could suspect that he would dare to undertake such
things, and accordingly his enemies were never prepared to
guard against his attacks. Aye, had he but worn the king's
colors and served under the rules of honest war, he might have
become as great and as renowned as Admiral Blake himself.

But all that is neither here nor there; what I have to tell
you now is that Captain Morgan in this open boat with his
twenty mates reached the Cape of Salmedina toward the fall
of day. Arriving within view of the harbor they discovered the
plate fleet at anchor, with two men-of-war and an armed galley
riding as a guard at the mouth of the harbor, scarce half a
league distant from the other ships. Having spied the fleet in
this posture, the pirates presently pulled down their sails and
rowed along the coast, feigning to be a Spanish vessel from
Nombre de Dios. So hugging the shore, they came boldly

within the harbor, upon the opposite side of which you might see the fortress a considerable distance away.

Being now come so near to the consummation of their adventure, Captain Morgan required every man to make an oath to stand by him to the last, whereunto our hero swore as heartily as any man aboard, although his heart, I must needs confess, was beating at a great rate at the approach of what was to happen. Having thus received the oaths of all his followers, Captain Morgan commanded the surgeon of the expedition that, when the order was given, he, the medico, was to bore six holes in the boat, so that, it sinking under them, they might all be compelled to push forward, with no chance of retreat. And such was the ascendancy of this man over his followers, and such was their awe of him, that not one of them uttered even so much as a murmur, though what he had commanded the surgeon to do pledged them either to victory or to death, with no chance to choose between. Nor did the surgeon question the orders he had received, much less did he dream of disobeying them.

By now it had fallen pretty dusk, whereupon, spying two fishermen in a canoe at a little distance, Captain Morgan demanded of them in Spanish which vessel of those at anchor in the harbor was the vice admiral, for that he had dispatches for the captain thereof. Whereupon the fishermen, suspecting nothing, pointed to them a galleon of great size riding at anchor not half a league distant.

Toward this vessel accordingly the pirates directed their course, and when they had come pretty nigh, Captain Morgan called upon the surgeon that now it was time for him to perform the duty that had been laid upon him. Whereupon the other did as he was ordered, and that so thoroughly that the water presently came gushing into the boat in great streams, whereat all hands pulled for the galleon as though every next moment was to be their last.

And what do you suppose were our hero's emotions at this time? Like all in the boat, his awe of Captain Morgan was so great that I do believe he would rather have gone to the bottom than have questioned his command, even when it was to scuttle the boat. Nevertheless, when he felt the cold water gushing about his feet (for he had taken off his shoes and stockings) he became possessed with such a fear of being drowned that even the Spanish galleon had no terrors for him if he could only feel the solid planks thereof beneath his feet.

Indeed, all the crew appeared to be possessed of a like dismay, for they pulled at the oars with such an incredible force that they were under the quarter of the galleon before the boat was half filled with water.

Here, as they approached, it then being pretty dark and the moon not yet having risen, the watch upon the deck hailed them, whereupon Captain Morgan called out in Spanish that he was Capt. Alvarez Mendazo, and that he brought dispatches for the vice admiral.

But at that moment, the boat being now so full of water as to be logged, it suddenly tilted upon one side as though to sink beneath them, whereupon all hands, without further orders, went scrambling up the side, as nimble as so many monkeys, each armed with a pistol in one hand and a cutlass in the other, and so were upon deck before the watch could collect his wits to utter any outcry or to give any other alarm than to cry out, "Jesu bless us! who are these?" at which words somebody knocked him down with the butt of a pistol, though who it was our hero could not tell in the darkness and the hurry.

Before any of those upon deck could recover from their alarm or those from below come up upon deck, a part of the pirates, under the carpenter and the surgeon, had run to the gun room and had taken possession of the arms, while Captain Morgan, with Master Harry and a Portuguese called Murillo Braziliano, had flown with the speed of the wind into the great cabin.

Here they found the captain of the vice admiral playing at cards with the Sieur Simon and a friend, Madam Simon and her daughter being present.

Captain Morgan instantly set his pistol at the breast of the Spanish captain, swearing with a most horrible fierce countenance that if he spake a word or made any outcry he was a dead man. As for our hero, having now got his hand into the game, he performed the same service for the Spaniard's friend, declaring he would shoot him dead if he opened his lips or lifted so much as a single finger.

All this while the ladies, not comprehending what had occurred, had sat as mute as stones; but now having so far recovered themselves as to find a voice, the younger of the two fell to screaming, at which the Sieur Simon called out to her to be still, for these were friends who had come to help them, and not enemies who had come to harm them.

All this, you are to understand, occupied only a little while, for in less than a minute three or four of the pirates had come into the cabin, who, together with the Portuguese, proceeded at once to bind the two Spaniards hand and foot, and to gag them. This being done to our buccaneer's satisfaction, and the Spanish captain being stretched out in the corner of the cabin, he instantly cleared his countenance of its terrors, and bursting forth into a great loud laugh, clapped his hand to the Sieur Simon's, which he wrung with the best will in the world. Having done this, and being in a fine humor after this his first success, he turned to the two ladies. "And this, ladies," said he, taking our hero by the hand and presenting him, "is a young gentleman who has embarked with me to learn the trade of piracy. I recommend him to your politeness."

Think what a confusion this threw our Master Harry into, to be sure, who at his best was never easy in the company of strange ladies! You may suppose what must have been his emotions to find himself thus introduced to the attention of Madam Simon and her daughter, being at the time in his bare feet, clad only in his shirt and breeches, and with no hat upon his head, a pistol in one hand and a cutlass in the other. However, he was not left for long to his embarrassments, for almost immediately after he had thus far relaxed, Captain Morgan fell of a sudden serious again, and bidding the Sieur Simon to get his ladies away into some place of safety, for the most hazardous part of this adventure was yet to occur, he quitted the cabin with Master Harry and the other pirates (for you may call him a pirate now) at his heels.

Having come upon deck, our hero beheld that a part of the Spanish crew were huddled forward in a flock like so many sheep (the others being crowded below with the hatches fastened upon them), and such was the terror of the pirates, and so dreadful the name of Henry Morgan, that not one of those poor wretches dared to lift up his voice to give any alarm, nor even to attempt an escape by jumping overboard.

At Captain Morgan's orders, these men, together with certain of his own company, ran nimbly aloft and began setting the sails, which, the night now having fallen pretty thick, was not for a good while observed by any of the vessels riding at anchor about them.

Indeed, the pirates might have made good their escape, with at most only a shot or two from the men-of-war, had it not then been about the full of the moon, which, having arisen, presently discovered to those of the fleet that lay closest about them what was being done aboard the vice admiral.

At this one of the vessels hailed them, and then after a while, having no reply, hailed them again. Even then the Spaniards might not immediately have suspected anything was amiss but only that the vice admiral for some reason best known to himself was shifting his anchorage, had not one of the Spaniards aloft—but who it was Captain Morgan was never able to discover—answered the hail by crying out that the vice admiral had been seized by the pirates.

At this the alarm was instantly given and the mischief done, for presently there was a tremendous bustle through that part of the fleet lying nighest the vice admiral—a deal of shouting of orders, a beating of drums, and the running hither and thither of the crews.

But by this time the sails of the vice admiral had filled with a strong land breeze that was blowing up the harbor, whereupon the carpenter, at Captain Morgan's orders, having cut away both anchors, the galleon presently bore away up the harbor, gathering headway every moment with the wind nearly dead astern. The nearest vessel was the only one that for the moment was able to offer any hindrance. This ship, having by this time cleared away one of its guns, was able to fire a parting shot against the vice-admiral, striking her somewhere forward, as our hero could see by a great shower of splinters that flew up in the moonlight.

At the sound of the shot all the vessels of the flota not yet disturbed by the alarm were aroused at once, so that the pirates had the satisfaction of knowing that they would have to run the gantlet of all the ships between them and the open sea before they could reckon themselves escaped.

And, indeed, to our hero's mind it seemed that the battle

which followed must have been the most terrific cannonade that was ever heard in the world. It was not so ill at first, for it was some while before the Spaniards could get their guns clear for action, they being not the least in the world prepared for such an occasion as this. But by and by first one and then another ship opened fire upon the galleon, until it seemed to our hero that all the thunders of heaven let loose upon them could not have created a more prodigious uproar, and that it was not possible that they could any of them escape destruction.

By now the moon had risen full and round, so that the clouds of smoke that rose in the air appeared as white as snow. The air seemed full of the hiss and screaming of shot, each one of which, when it struck the galleon, was magnified by our hero's imagination into ten times its magnitude from the crash which it delivered and from the cloud of splinters it would cast up into the moonlight. At last he suddenly beheld one poor man knocked sprawling across the deck, who, as he raised his arm from behind the mast, disclosed that the hand was gone from it, and that the shirt sleeve was red with blood in the moonlight. At this sight all the strength fell away from poor Harry, and he felt sure that a like fate or even a worse must be in store for him.

But, after all, this was nothing to what it might have been in broad daylight, for what with the darkness of night, and the little preparation the Spaniards could make for such a business, and the extreme haste with which they discharged their guns (many not understanding what was the occasion of all this uproar), nearly all the shot flew so wide of the mark that not above one in twenty struck that at which it was aimed.

Meantime Captain Morgan, with the Sieur Simon, who had followed him upon deck, stood just above where our hero lay behind the shelter of the bulwark. The captain had lit a pipe of tobacco, and he stood now in the bright moonlight close to the rail, with his hands behind him, looking out ahead with the utmost coolness imaginable, and paying no more attention to the din of battle than though it were twenty leagues away. Now and then he would take his pipe from his lips to utter an order to the man at the wheel. Excepting this he stood there hardly moving at all, the wind blowing his long red hair over his shoulders.

Had it not been for the armed galley the pirates might have got the galleon away with no great harm done in spite of all this cannonading, for the man-of-war which rode at anchor nighest to them at the mouth of the harbor was still so far away that they might have passed it by hugging pretty close to the shore, and that without any great harm being done to them in the darkness. But just at this moment, when the open water lay in sight, came this galley pulling out from behind the point of the shore in such a manner as either to head our pirates off entirely or else to comple them to approach so near to the man-of-war that the latter vessel could bring its guns to bear with more effect.

This galley, I must tell you, was like others of its kind such as you may find in these waters, the hull being long and cut low to the water so as to allow the oars to dip freely. The bow was sharp and projected far out ahead, mounting a swivel upon it, while at the stern a number of galleries built one above another into a castle gave shelter to several companies of musketeers as well as the officers commanding them.

Our hero could behold the approach of this gallery from above the starboard bulwarks, and it appeared to him impossible for them to hope to escape either it or the man-of-war. But still Captain Morgan maintained the same composure that he had exhibited all the while, only now and then delivering an order to the man at the wheel, who, putting the helm over, threw the bows of the galleon around more to the larboard, as though to escape the bow of the galley and get into the open water beyond. This course brought the pirates ever closer and closer to the man-of-war, which now began to add its thunder to the din of the battle, and with so much more effect that at every discharge you might hear the crashing and crackling of splintered wood, and now and then the outcry or groaning of some man who was hurt. Indeed, had it been daylight, they must at this juncture all have perished, though, as was said, what with the night and the confusion and the hurry, they escaped entire destruction, though more by a miracle than through any policy upon their own part.

Meantime the galley, steering as though to come aboard of them, had now come so near that it, too, presently began to open its musketry fire upon them, so that the humming and rattling of bullets were presently added to the din of cannonading.

In two minutes more it would have been aboard of them, when in a moment Captain Morgan roared out of a sudden to the man at the helm to put it hard a starboard. In response the man ran the wheel over with the utmost quickness, and the galleon, obeying her helm very readily, came around upon a course which, if continued, would certainly bring them into collision with their enemy.

It is possible at first the Spaniards imagined the pirates intended to escape past their stern, for they instantly began backing oars to keep them from getting past, so that the water was all of a foam about them; at the same time they did this they poured in such a fire of musketry that it was a miracle that no more execution was accomplished than happened.

As for our hero, methinks for the moment he forgot all about everything else than as to whether or no his captain's maneuver would succeed, for in the very first moment he divined, as by some instinct, what Captain Morgan purposed doing.

At this moment, so particular in the execution of this nice design, a bullet suddenly struck down the man at the wheel. Hearing the sharp outcry, our Harry turned to see him fall forward, and then to his hands and knees upon the deck, the blood running in a black pool beneath him, while the wheel, escaping from his hands, spun over until the spokes were all of a mist.

In a moment the ship would have fallen off before the wind had not our hero, leaping to the wheel (even as Captain Morgan shouted an order for some one to do so), seized the flying spokes, whirling them back again, and so bringing the bow of the galleon up to its former course.

In the first moment of this effort he had reckoned of nothing but of carrying out his captain's designs. He neither thought of cannon balls nor of bullets. But now that his task was accomplished, he came suddenly back to himself to find the galleries of the galley aflame with musket shots, and to become aware with a most horrible sinking of the spirits that all the shots therefrom were intended for him. He cast his eyes about him with despair, but no one came to ease him of his task, which, having undertaken, he had too much spirit to resign from carrying through to the end, though he was well aware that the very next instant might mean his sudden and violent death. His ears hummed and rang, and his brain swam as light as a feather. I know not whether he breathed, but he shut his eyes tight as though that might save him from the bullets that were raining about him.

At this moment the Spaniards must have discovered for the first time the pirates' design, for of a sudden they ceased firing, and began to shout out a multitude of orders, while the oars lashed the water all about with a foam. But it was too late then for them to escape, for within a couple of seconds the galleon struck her enemy a blow so violent upon the larboard quarter as nearly to hurl our Harry upon the deck, and then with a dreadful, horrible crackling of wood, commingled with a yelling of men's voices, the galley was swung around upon her side, and the galleon, sailing into the open sea, left nothing of her immediate enemy but a sinking wreck, and the water dotted all over with bobbing heads and waving hands in the moonlight.

And now, indeed, that all danger was past and gone, there were plenty to come running to help our hero at the wheel. As for Captain Morgan, having come down upon the main deck, he fetches the young helmsman a clap upon the back. "Well, Master Harry," says he, "and did I not tell you I would make a man of you?" Whereat our poor Harry fell a-laughing, but with a sad catch in his voice, for his hands trembled as with an ague, and were as cold as ice. As for his emotions, God knows he was nearer crying than laughing, if Captain Morgan had but known it.

Nevertheless, though undertaken under the spur of the moment, I protest it was indeed a brave deed, and I cannot but wonder how many young gentlemen of sixteen there are to-day who, upon a like occasion, would act as well as our Harry.

5

The balance of our hero's adventures were of a lighter sort than those already recounted, for the next morning the Spanish captain (a very polite and well-bred gentleman) having fitted him out with a shift of his own clothes, Master Harry was presented in a proper form to the ladies. For Captain Morgan, if he had felt a liking for the young man before, could not now show sufficient regard for him. He ate in the great cabin and was petted by all. Madam Simon, who was a fat and red-faced lady, was forever praising him, and the young miss, who was extremely well-looking, was as continually making eyes at him.

She and Master Harry, I must tell you, would spend hours together, she making pretense of teaching him French, although he was so possessed with a passion of love that he was nigh suffocated with it. She, upon her part, perceiving his emotions, responded with extreme good nature and complacency, so that had our hero been older, and the voyage proved longer, he might have become entirely enmeshed in the toils of his fair siren. For all this while, you are to understand, the pirates were making sail straight for Jamaica, which they reached upon the third day in perfect safety.

In that time, however, the pirates had well-nigh gone crazy for joy; for when they came to examine their purchase they discovered her cargo to consist of plate to the prodigious sum of £130,000 in value. 'Twas a wonder they did not all make themselves drunk for joy. No doubt they would have done so had not Captain Morgan, knowing they were still in the exact track of the Spanish fleets, threatened them that the first man among them who touched a drop of rum without his permission he would shoot him dead upon the deck. This threat had such effect that they all remained entirely sober until they had reached Port Royal Harbor, which they did about nine o'clock in the morning.

And now it was that our hero's romance came all tumbling down about his ears with a run. For they had hardly come to anchor in the harbor when a boat came from a man-of-war, and who should come stepping aboard but Lieutenant Grantley (a particular friend of our hero's father) and his own eldest brother Thomas, who, putting on a very stern face, informed Master Harry that he was a desperate and hardened villain who was sure to end at the gallows, and that he was to go immediately back to his home again. He told our embryo pirate that his family had nigh gone distracted because of his wicked and ungrateful conduct. Nor could our hero move him from his inflexible purpose. "What," says our Harry, "and will you not then let me wait until our prize is divided and I get my share?"

"Prize, indeed!" says his brother. "And do you then really think that your father would consent to your having a share in this terrible bloody and murthering business?"

And so, after a good deal of argument, our hero was constrained to go; nor did he even have an opportunity to bid adieu to his inamorata. Nor did he see her any more, except from a distance, she standing on the poop deck as he was rowed away from her, her face all stained with crying. For himself, he felt that there was no more joy in life; nevertheless,

101

standing up in the stern of the boat, he made shift, though with an aching heart, to deliver her a fine bow with the hat he had borrowed from the Spanish captain, before his brother bade him sit down again.

And so to the ending of this story, with only this to relate, that our Master Harry, so far from going to the gallows, became in good time a respectable and wealthy sugar merchant with an English wife and a fine family of children, whereunto, when the mood was upon him, he has sometimes told these adventures (and sundry others not here recounted), as I have told them unto you.

IV

TOM CHIST AND THE TREASURE BOX

An Old-time Story of the Days of Captain Kidd

1

O tell about Tom Chist, and how he got his name, and how he came to be living at the little settlement of Henlopen, just inside the mouth of the Delaware Bay, the story must begin as far back as 1686, when a great storm swept the Atlantic coast from end to end. During the heaviest part of the hurricane a bark went ashore on the Hen-and-Chicken Shoals, just below Cape Henlopen and at the mouth of the Delaware Bay, and Tom Chist was the only soul of all those on board the ill-fated vessel who escaped alive.

This story must first be told, because it was on account of the strange and miraculous escape that happened to him at that time that he gained the name that was given to him.

Even as late as that time of the American colonies, the little scattered settlement at Henlopen, made up of English, with a few Dutch and Swedish people, was still only a spot upon the face of the great American wilderness that spread away, with swamp and forest, no man knew how far to the westward. That wilderness was not only full of wild beasts, but of Indian savages, who every fall would come in wandering tribes to spend the winter along the shores of the fresh-water lakes below Henlopen. There for four or five months they would live upon fish and clams and wild ducks and geese, chipping their arrowheads, and making their earthenware pots and pans under the lee of the sand hills and pine woods below the Capes.

Sometimes on Sundays, when the Rev. Hillary Jones would be preaching in the little log church back in the woods, these half-clad red savages would come in from the cold, and sit squatting in the back part of the church, listening stolidly to the words that had no meaning for them.

But about the wreck of the bark in 1686. Such a wreck as that which then went ashore on the Hen-and-Chicken Shoals was a godsend to the poor and needy settlers in the wilderness where so few good things ever came. For the vessel went to pieces during the night, and the next morning the beach was strewn with wreckage—boxes and barrels, chests and spars, timbers and planks, a plentiful and bountiful harvest, to be gathered up by the settlers as they chose, with no one to forbid or prevent them.

The name of the bark, as found painted on some of the water barrels and sea chests, was the *Bristol Merchant,* and she no doubt hailed from England.

As was said, the only soul who escaped alive off the wreck was Tom Chist.

A settler, a fisherman named Matt Abrahamson, and his daughter Molly, found Tom. He was washed up on the beach among the wreckage, in a great wooden box which had been securely tied around with a rope and lashed between two spars—apparently for better protection in beating through the surf. Matt Abrahamson thought he had found something of more than usual value when he came upon this chest; but when he cut the cords and broke open the box with his broadax, he could not have been more astonished had he beheld a salamander instead of a baby of nine or ten months old lying half smothered in the blankets that covered the bottom of the chest.

Matt Abrahamson's daughter Molly had had a baby who had died a month or so before. So when she saw the little one lying there in the bottom of the chest, she cried out in a great loud voice that the Good Man had sent her another baby in place of her own.

The rain was driving before the hurricane storm in dim, slanting sheets, and so she wrapped up the baby in the man's coat she wore and ran off home without waiting to gather up any more of the wreckage.

It was Parson Jones who gave the foundling his name. When the news came to his ears of what Matt Abrahamson had found he went over to the fisherman's cabin to see the child. He examined the clothes in which the baby was dressed. They were of fine linen and handsomely stitched, and the reverend gentleman opined that the foundling's parents must have been of quality. A kerchief had been wrapped around the baby's neck and under its arms and tied behind, and in the corner, marked with very fine needlework, were the initials T. C.

"What d'ye call him, Molly?" said Parson Jones. He was standing, as he spoke, with his back to the fire, warming his palms before the blaze. The pocket of the greatcoat he wore bulged out with a big case bottle of spirits which he had gath-

105

ered up out of the wreck that afternoon. "What d'ye call him, Molly?"

"I'll call him Tom, after my own baby."

"That goes very well with the initial on the kerchief," said Parson Jones. "But what other name d'ye give him? Let it be something to go with the C."

"I don't know," said Molly.

"Why not call him 'Chist,' since he was born in a chist out of the sea? 'Tom Chist'—the name goes off like a flash in the pan." And so "Tom Chist" he was called and "Tom Chist" he was christened.

So much for the beginning of the history of Tom Chist. The story of Captain Kidd's treasure box does not begin until the late spring of 1699.

That was the year that the famous pirate captain, coming up from the West Indies, sailed his sloop into the Delaware Bay, where he lay for over a month waiting for news from his friends in New York.

For he had sent word to that town asking if the coast was clear for him to return home with the rich prize he had brought from the Indian seas and the coast of Africa, and meantime he lay there in the Delaware Bay waiting for a reply. Before he left he turned the whole of Tom Chist's life topsy-turvy with something that he brought ashore.

By that time Tom Chist had grown into a strong-limbed, thick-jointed boy of fourteen or fifteen years of age. It was a miserable dog's life he lived with old Matt Abrahamson, for the old fisherman was in his cups more than half the time, and when he was so there was hardly a day passed that he did not give Tom a curse or a buffet or, as like as not, an actual beating. One would have thought that such treatment would have broken the spirit of the poor little foundling, but it had just the opposite effect upon Tom Chist, who was one of your stubborn, sturdy, stiff-willed fellows who only grow harder and more tough the more they are ill-treated. It had been a long time now since he had made any outcry or complaint at the hard usage he suffered from old Matt. At such times he would shut his teeth and bear whatever came to him, until sometimes the half-drunken old man would be driven almost mad by his stubborn silence. Maybe he would stop in the midst of the beating he was administering, and, grinding his teeth, would cry out: "Won't ye say naught? Won't ye say naught? Well, then, I'll see if I can't make ye say naught." When things had reached such a pass as this Molly would generally interfere to protect her foster son, and then she and Tom would together fight the old man until they had wrenched the stick or the strap out of his hand. Then old Matt would chase them out of doors and around and around the house for maybe half an hour, until his anger was cool, when he would go back again, and for a time the storm would be over.

Besides his foster mother, Tom Chist had a very good friend in Parson Jones, who used to come over every now and then to Abrahamson's hut upon the chance of getting a half dozen fish for breakfast. He always had a kind word or two for Tom, who during the winter evenings would go over to the good man's house to learn his letters, and to read and write and cipher a little, so that by now he was able to spell the words out of the Bible and the almanac, and knew enough to change tuppence into four ha'pennies.

This is the sort of boy Tom Chist was, and this is the sort of life he led.

In the late spring or early summer of 1699 Captain Kidd's sloop sailed into the mouth of the Delaware Bay and changed the whole fortune of his life.

And this is how you come to the story of Captain Kidd's treasure box.

2

Old Matt Abrahamson kept the flat-bottomed boat in which he went fishing some distance down the shore, and in the neighborhood of the old wreck that had been sunk on the Shoals. This was the usual fishing ground of the settlers, and here old Matt's boat generally lay drawn up on the sand.

There had been a thunderstorm that afternoon, and Tom had gone down the beach to bale out the boat in readiness for the morning's fishing.

It was full moonlight now, as he was returning, and the night sky was full of floating clouds. Now and then there was a dull flash to the westward, and once a muttering growl of thunder, promising another storm to come.

All that day the pirate sloop had been lying just off the shore back of the Capes, and now Tom Chist could see the sails glimmering pallidly in the moonlight, spread for drying after the storm. He was walking up the shore homeward when he became aware that at some distance ahead of him there was a ship's boat drawn up on a little narrow beach, and a group of men clustered about it. He hurried forward with a good deal of curiosity to see who had landed, but it was not until he had come close to them that he could distinguish who and what they were. Then he knew that it must be a party who had come off the pirate sloop. They had evidently just landed, and two men were lifting out a chest from the boat. One of them was a negro, naked to the waist, and the other was a white man in his shirt sleeves, wearing petticoat breeches, a Monterey cap upon his head, a red bandanna handkerchief around his neck, and gold earrings in his ears. He had a long, plaited queue hanging down his back, and a great sheath knife dangling from his side. Another man, evidently the captain of the party, stood at a little distance as they lifted the chest out of the boat. He had a cane in one hand and a lighted lantern

108

in the other, although the moon was shining as bright as day. He wore jack boots and a handsome laced coat, and he had a long, drooping mustache that curled down below his chin. He wore a fine, feathered hat, and his long black hair hung down upon his shoulders.

All this Tom Chist could see in the moonlight that glinted and twinkled upon the gilt buttons of his coat.

They were so busy lifting the chest from the boat that at first they did not observe that Tom Chist had come up and was standing there. It was the white man with the long, plaited queue and the gold earrings that spoke to him. "Boy, what do you want here, boy?" he said, in a rough, hoarse voice. "Where d'ye come from?" And then dropping his end of the chest, and without giving Tom time to answer, he pointed off down the beach, and said, "You'd better be going about your own business, if you know what's good for you; and don't you come back, or you'll find what you don't want waiting for you."

Tom saw in a glance that the pirates were all looking at him, and then, without saying a word, he turned and walked away. The man who had spoken to him followed him threateningly for some little distance, as though to see that he had gone away as he was bidden to do. But presently he stopped, and Tom hurried on alone, until the boat and the crew and all were dropped away behind and lost in the moonlight night. Then he himself stopped also, turned, and looked back whence he had come.

There had been something very strange in the appearance of the men he had just seen, something very mysterious in their actions, and he wondered what it all meant, and what they were going to do. He stood for a little while thus looking and listening. He could see nothing, and could hear only the sound of distant talking. What were they doing on the lonely shore thus at night? Then, following a sudden impulse. he

109

turned and cut off across the sand hummocks, skirting around inland, but keeping pretty close to the shore, his object being to spy upon them, and to watch what they were about from the back of the low sand hills that fronted the beach.

He had gone along some distance in his circuitous return when he became aware of the sound of voices that seemed to be drawing closer to him as he came toward the speakers. He stopped and stood listening, and instantly, as he stopped, the voices stopped also. He crouched there silently in the bright, glimmering moonlight, surrounded by the silent stretches of sand, and the stillness seemed to press upon him like a heavy hand. Then suddenly the sound of a man's voice began again, and as Tom listened he could hear some one slowly counting "Ninety-one," the voice began, "ninety-two, ninety-three, ninety-four, ninety-five, ninety-six, ninety-seven, ninety-eight, ninety-nine, one hundred, one hundred and one"—the slow, monotonous count coming nearer and nearer; "one hundred and two, one hundred and three, one hundred and four," and so on in its monotonous reckoning.

Suddenly he saw three heads appear above the sand hill, so close to him that he crouched down quickly with a keen thrill, close beside the hummock near which he stood. His first fear was that they might have seen him in the moonlight; but they had not, and his heart rose again as the counting voice went steadily on. "One hundred and twenty," it was say-ing—"and twenty-one, and twenty-two, and twenty-three, and twenty-four," and then he who was counting came out from behind the little sandy rise into the white and open level of shimmering brightness.

It was the man with the cane whom Tom had seen some time before—the captain of the party who had landed. He carried his cane under his arm now, and was holding his lantern close to something that he held in his hand, and upon which

110

he looked narrowly as he walked with a slow and measured
tread in a perfectly straight line across the sand, counting each
step as he took it. "And twenty-five, and twenty-six, and
twenty-seven, and twenty-eight, and twenty-nine, and thirty."

Behind him walked two other figures; one was the half-
naked negro, the other the man with the plaited queue and
the earrings, whom Tom had seen lifting the chest out of the
boat. Now they were carrying the heavy box between them,
laboring through the sand with shuffling tread as they bore
it onward. As he who was counting pronounced the word
"thirty," the two men set the chest down on the sand with a
grunt, the white man panting and blowing and wiping his
sleeve across his forehead. And immediately he who counted
took out a slip of paper and marked something down upon
it. They stood there for a long time, during which Tom lay
behind the sand hummock watching them, and for a while the
silence was uninterrupted. In the perfect stillness Tom could
hear the washing of the little waves beating upon the distant
beach, and once the far-away sound of a laugh from one of
those who stood by the ship's boat.

One, two, three minutes passed, and then the men picked
up the chest and started on again; and then again the other
man begin his counting. "Thirty and one, and thirty and two,
and thirty and three, and thirty and four"—he walked straight
across the level open, still looking intently at that which he
held in his hand—"and thirty and five, and thirty and six, and
thirty and seven," and so on, until the three figures disappeared in the little hollow between the two sand hills on the
opposite side of the open, and still Tom could hear the sound
of the counting voice in the distance.

Just as they disappeared behind the hill there was a sudden
faint flash of light; and by and by, as Tom lay still listening to
the counting, he heard, after a long interval, a far-away muffled

rumble of distant thunder. He waited for a while, and then arose and stepped to the top of the sand hummock behind which he had been lying. He looked all about him, but there was no one else to be seen. Then he stepped down from the hummock and followed in the direction which the pirate captain and the two men carrying the chest had gone. He crept along cautiously, stopping now and then to make sure that he still heard the counting voice, and when it ceased he lay down upon the sand and waited until it began again.

Presently, so following the pirates, he saw the three figures again in the distance, and, skirting around back of a hill of sand covered with coarse sedge grass, he came to where he overlooked a little open level space gleaming white in the moonlight.

The three had been crossing the level of sand, and were now not more than twenty-five paces from him. They had again set down the chest, upon which the white man with the long queue and the gold earrings had seated to rest himself, the negro standing close beside him. The moon shone as bright as day and full upon his face. It was looking directly at Tom Chist, every line as keen cut with white lights and black shadows as though it had been carved in ivory and jet. He sat perfectly motionless, and Tom drew back with a start, almost thinking he had been discovered. He lay silent, his heart beating heavily in his throat; but there was no alarm, and presently he heard the counting begin again, and when he looked once more he saw they were going away straight across the little open. A soft, sliding hillock of sand lay directly in front of them. They did not turn aside, but went straight over it, the leader helping himself up the sandy slope with his cane, still counting and still keeping his eyes fixed upon that which he held in his hand. Then they disappeared again behind the white crest on the other side.

So Tom followed them cautiously until they had gone almost half a mile inland. When next he saw them clearly it was from a little sandy rise which looked down like the crest of a bowl upon the floor of sand below. Upon this smooth, white floor the moon beat with almost dazzling brightness.

The white man who had helped to carry the chest was now kneeling, busied at some work, though what it was Tom at first could not see. He was whittling the point of a stick into a long wooden peg, and when, by and by, he had finished what he was about, he arose and stepped to where he who seemed to be the captain had stuck his cane upright into the ground as though to mark some particular spot. He drew the cane out of the sand, thrusting the stick down in its stead. Then he drove the long peg down with a wooden mallet which the negro handed to him. The sharp rapping of the mallet upon the top of the peg sounded loud in the perfect stillness, and Tom lay watching and wondering what it all meant. The man, with quick-repeated blows, drove the peg farther and farther down into the sand until it showed only two or three inches above the surface. As he finished his work there was another faint flash of light, and by and by another smothered rumble of thunder, and Tom, as he looked out toward the westward, saw the silver rim of the round and sharply outlined thundercloud rising slowly up into the sky and pushing the other and broken drifting clouds before it.

The two white men were now stooping over the peg, the negro man watching them. Then presently the man with the cane started straight away from the peg, carrying the end of a measuring line with him, the other end of which the man with the plaited queue held against the top of the peg. When the pirate captain had reached the end of the measuring line he marked a cross upon the sand, and then again they measured out another stretch of space.

113

So they measured a distance five times over, and then, from where Tom lay, he could see the man with the queue drive another peg just at the foot of a sloping rise of sand that swept up beyond into a tall white dune marked sharp and clear against the night sky behind. As soon as the man with the plaited queue had driven the second peg into the ground they began measuring again, and so, still measuring, disappeared in another direction which took them in behind the sand dune where Tom no longer could see what they were doing.

The negro still sat by the chest where the two had left him, and so bright was the moonlight that from where he lay Tom could see the glint of it twinkling in the whites of his eyeballs.

Presently from behind the hill there came, for the third time, the sharp rapping sound of the mallet driving still another peg, and then after a while the two pirates emerged from behind the sloping whiteness into the space of moonlight again.

They came direct to where the chest lay, and the white man and the black man lifting it once more, they walked away across the level of open sand, and so on behind the edge of the hill and out of Tom's sight.

3

Tom Chist could no longer see what the pirates were doing, neither did he dare to cross over the open space of sand that now lay between them and him. He lay there speculating as to what they were about, and meantime the storm cloud was rising higher and higher above the horizon, with louder and louder mutterings of thunder following each dull flash from out the cloudy, cavernous depths. In the silence he could hear an occasional click as of some iron implement, and he opined that the pirates were burying the chest, though just where they were at work he could neither see nor tell.

114

Still he lay there watching and listening, and by and by a puff of warm air blew across the sand, and a thumping tumble of louder thunder leaped from out the belly of the storm cloud, which every minute was coming nearer and nearer. Still Tom Chist lay watching.

Suddenly, almost unexpectedly, the three figures reappeared from behind the sand hill, the pirate captain leading the way, and the negro and white man following close behind him. They had gone about halfway across the white, sandy level between the hill and the hummock behind which Tom Chist lay, when the white man stopped and bent over as though to tie his shoe.

This brought the negro a few steps in front of his companion.

That which then followed happened so suddenly, so unexpectedly, so swiftly, that Tom Chist had hardly time to realize what it all meant before it was over. As the negro passed him the white man arose suddenly and silently erect, and Tom Chist saw the white moonlight glint upon the blade of a great dirk knife which he now held in his hand. He took one, two silent, catlike steps behind the unsuspecting negro. Then there was a sweeping flash of the blade in the pallid light, and a blow, the thump of which Tom could distinctly hear even from where he lay stretched out upon the sand. There was an instant echoing yell from the black man, who ran stumbling forward, who stopped, who regained his footing, and then stood for an instant as though rooted to the spot.

Tom had distinctly seen the knife enter his back, and even thought that he had seen the glint of the point as it came out from the breast.

Meantime the pirate captain had stopped, and now stood with his hand resting upon his cane looking impasively on.

Then the black man started to run. The white man stood for a while glaring after him; then he, too, started after his

115

victim upon the run. The black man was not very far from Tom when he staggered and fell. He tried to rise, then fell forward again, and lay at length. At that instant the first edge of the cloud cut across the moon, and there was a sudden darkness; but in the silence Tom heard the sound of another blow and a groan, and then presently a voice calling to the pirate captain that it was all over.

He saw the dim form of the captain crossing the level sand, and then, as the moon sailed out from behind the cloud, he saw the white man standing over a black figure that lay motionless upon the sand.

Then Tom Chist scrambled up and ran away, plunging down into the hollow of sand that lay in the shadows below. Over the next rise he ran, and down again into the next black hollow, and so on over the sliding, shifting ground, panting and gasping. It seemed to him that he could hear footsteps following, and in the terror that possessed him he almost expected every instant to feel the cold knife blade slide between his own ribs in such a thrust from behind as he had seen given to the poor black man.

So he ran on like one in a nightmare. His feet grew heavy

like lead, he panted and gasped, his breath came hot and dry in his throat. But still he ran and ran until at last he found himself in front of old Matt Abrahamson's cabin, gasping, panting, and sobbing for breath, his knees relaxed and his thighs trembling with weakness.

As he opened the door and dashed into the darkened cabin (for both Matt and Molly were long ago asleep in bed) there was a flash of light, and even as he slammed to the door behind him there was an instant peal of thunder, heavy as though a great weight had been dropped upon the roof of the sky, so that the doors and windows of the cabin rattled.

4

Then Tom Chist crept to bed, trembling, shuddering, bathed in sweat, his heart beating like a trip hammer, and his brain dizzy from that long, terror-inspired race through the soft sand in which he had striven to outstrip he knew not what pursuing horror.

For a long, long time he lay awake, trembling and chattering with nervous chills, and when he did fall asleep it was only to drop into monstrous dreams in which he once again saw ever enacted, with various grotesque variations, the tragic drama which his waking eyes had beheld the night before.

Then came the dawning of the broad, wet daylight, and before the rising of the sun Tom was up and out of doors to find the young day dripping with the rain of overnight.

His first act was to climb the nearest sand hill and to gaze out toward the offing where the pirate ship had been the day before.

It was no longer there.

Soon afterward Matt Abrahamson came out of the cabin and he called to Tom to go get a bite to eat, for it was time for them to be away fishing.

117

All that morning the recollection of the night before hung over Tom Chist like a great cloud of boding trouble. It filled the confined area of the little boat and spread over the entire wide spaces of sky and sea that surrounded them. Not for a moment was it lifted. Even when he was hauling in his wet and dripping line with a struggling fish at the end of it a recurrent memory of what he had seen would suddenly come upon him, and he would groan in spirit at the recollection. He looked at Matt Abrahamson's leathery face, at his lantern jaws cavernously and stolidly chewing at a tobacco leaf, and it seemed monstrous to him that the old man should be so unconscious of the black cloud that wrapped them all about.

When the boat reached the shore again he leaped scrambling to the beach, and as soon as his dinner was eaten he hurried away to find the Dominie Jones.

He ran all the way from Abrahamson's hut to the parson's house, hardly stopping once, and when he knocked at the door he was panting and sobbing for breath.

The good man was sitting on the back-kitchen doorstep smoking his long pipe of tobacco out into the sunlight, while his wife within was rattling about among the pans and dishes in preparation of their supper, of which a strong, porky smell already filled the air.

Then Tom Chist told his story, panting, hurrying, tumbling one word over another in his haste, and Parson Jones listened, breaking every now and then into an ejaculation of wonder. The light in his pipe went out and the bowl turned cold.

"And I don't see why they should have killed the poor black man," said Tom, as he finished his narrative.

"Why, that is very easy enough to understand," said the good reverend man. " 'Twas a treasure box they buried!"

In his agitation Mr. Jones had risen from his seat and was

118

now stumping up and down, puffing at his empty tobacco pipe as though it were still alight.

"A treasure box!" cried out Tom.

"Aye, a treasure box! And that was why they killed the poor black man. He was the only one, d'ye see, besides they two who knew the place where 'twas hid, and now that they've killed him out of the way, there's nobody but themselves knows. The villains— Tut, tut, look at that now!" In his excitement the dominie had snapped the stem of his tobacco pipe in two.

"Why, then," said Tom, "if that is so, 'tis indeed a wicked, bloody treasure, and fit to bring a curse upon anybody who finds it!"

" 'Tis more like to bring a curse upon the soul who buried it," said Parson Jones, "and it may be a blessing to him who finds it. But tell me, Tom, do you think you could find the place again where 'twas hid?"

"I can't tell that," said Tom, " 'twas all in among the sand humps, d'ye see, and it was at night into the bargain. Maybe we could find the marks of their feet in the sand," he added.

" 'Tis not likely," said the reverend gentleman, "for the storm last night would have washed all that away."

"I could find the place," said Tom, "where the boat was drawn up on the beach."

"Why, then, that's something to start from, Tom," said his friend. "If we can find that, then maybe we can find whither they went from there."

"If I was certain it was a treasure box," cried out Tom Chist, "I would rake over every foot of sand betwixt here and Henlopen to find it."

" 'Twould be like hunting for a pin in a haystack," said the Rev. Hilary Jones.

As Tom walked away home, it seemed as though a ton's

119

weight of gloom had been rolled away from his soul. The next day he and Parson Jones were to go treasure-hunting together; it seemed to Tom as though he could hardly wait for the time to come.

5

The next afternoon Parson Jones and Tom Chist started off together upon the expedition that made Tom's fortune forever. Tom carried a spade over his shoulder and the reverend gentleman walked along beside him with his cane.

As they jogged along up the beach they talked together about the only thing they could talk about—the treasure box. "And how big did you say 'twas?" quoth the good gentleman.

"About so long," said Tom Chist, measuring off upon the spade, "and about so wide, and this deep."

"And what if it should be full of money, Tom?" said the reverend gentleman, swinging his cane around and around in wide circles in the excitement of the thought, as he strode along briskly. "Suppose it should be full of money, what then?"

"By Moses!" said Tom Chist, hurrying to keep up with his friend, "I'd buy a ship for myself, I would, and I'd trade to Injy and to Chiny to my own boot, I would. Suppose the chist was all full of money, sir, and suppose we should find it; would there be enough in it, d'ye suppose, to buy a ship?"

"To be sure there would be enough, Tom enough and to spare, and a good big lump over."

"And if I find it 'tis mine to keep, is it, and no mistake?"

"Why, to be sure it would be yours!" cried out the parson, in a loud voice. "To be sure it would be yours!" He knew nothing of the law, but the doubt of the question began at once to ferment in his brain, and he strode along in silence for a while. "Whose else would it be but yours if you find it?" he burst out. "Can you tell me that?"

120

"If ever I have a ship of my own," said Tom Chist, "and if ever I sail to Injy in her, I'll fetch ye back the best chist of tea, sir, that ever was fetched from Cochin Chiny."

Parson Jones burst out laughing. "Thankee, Tom," he said; "and I'll thankee again when I get my chist of tea. But tell me, Tom, didst thou ever hear of the farmer girl who counted her chickens before they were hatched?"

It was thus they talked as they hurried along up the beach together, and so came to a place at last where Tom stopped short and stood looking about him. " 'Twas just here," he said, "I saw the boat last night. I know 'twas here, for I mind me of that bit of wreck yonder, and that there was a tall stake drove in the sand just where yon stake stands."

Parson Jones put on his barnacles and went over to the stake toward which Tom pointed. As soon as he had looked at it carefully he called out: "Why, Tom, this hath been just drove down into the sand. 'Tis a brand-new stake of wood, and the pirates must have set it here themselves as a mark, just as they drove the pegs you spoke about down into the sand."

Tom came over and looked at the stake. It was a stout piece of oak nearly two inches thick; it had been shaped with some care, and the top of it had been painted red. He shook the stake and tried to move it, but it had been driven or planted so deeply into the sand that he could not stir it. "Aye, sir," he said, "it must have been set here for a mark, for I'm sure 'twas not here yesterday or the day before." He stood looking about him to see if there were other signs of the pirates' presence. At some little distance there was the corner of something white sticking up out of the sand. He could see that it was a scrap of paper, and he pointed to it, calling out: "Yonder is a piece of paper, sir. I wonder if they left that behind them?"

It was a miraculous chance that placed that paper there. There was only an inch of it showing, and if it had not been for Tom's sharp eyes, it would certainly have been overlooked and passed by. The next windstorm would have covered it up, and all that afterward happened never would have occurred. "Look, sir," he said, as he struck the sand from it, "it hath writing on it."

"Let me see it," said Parson Jones. He adjusted the spectacles a little more firmly astride of his nose as he took the paper in his hand and began conning it. "What's all this?" he said; "a whole lot of figures and nothing else." And then he read aloud, " 'Mark—S. S. W. S. by S.' What d'ye suppose that means, Tom?"

"I don't know, sir," said Tom. "But maybe we can understand it better if you read on."

" 'Tis all a great lot of figures," said Parson Jones, "without a grain of meaning in them so far as I can see, unless they be sailing directions." And then he began reading again: " 'Mark —S. S. W. by S. 40, 72, 91, 130, 151, 177, 202, 232, 256, 271'—d'ye see, it must be sailing directions—'299, 335, 362, 386, 415, 446, 469, 491, 522, 544, 571, 598'—what a lot of them there be—'626, 652, 676, 695, 724, 851, 876, 905, 940, 967. Peg. S. E. by E. 269 foot. Peg. S. S. W. by S. 427 foot. Peg. Dig to the west of this six foot.' "

"What's that about a peg?" exclaimed Tom. "What's that about a peg? And then there's something about digging, too!" It was as though a sudden light began shining into his brain. He felt himself growing quickly very excited. "Read that over again, sir," he cried. "Why, sir, you remember I told you they drove a peg into the sand. And don't they say to dig close to it? Read it over again, sir—read it over again!"

"Peg?" said the good gentleman. "To be sure it was about a peg. Let's look again. Yes, here it is. 'Peg S. E. by E. 269 foot.' "

"Aye!" cried out Tom Chist again, in great excitement.

"Don't you remember what I told you, sir, 269 foot? Sure that must be what I saw 'em measuring with the line."

Parson Jones had now caught the flame of excitement that was blazing up so strongly in Tom's breast. He felt as though some wonderful thing was about to happen to them. "To be sure, to be sure!" he called out, in a great big voice. "And then they measured out 427 foot south-southwest by south, and they then drove another peg, and then they buried the box six foot to the west if it. Why, Tom—why, Tom Chist! if we've read this aright, thy fortune is made."

Tom Chist stood staring straight at the old gentleman's excited face, and seeing nothing but it in all the bright infinity of sunshine. Were they, indeed, about to find the treasure chest? He felt the sun very hot upon his shoulders, and he heard the harsh, insistent jarring of a tern that hovered and circled with forked tail and sharp white wings in the sunlight just above their heads; but all the time he stood staring into the good old gentleman's face.

It was Parson Jones who first spoke. "But what do all these figures mean?" And Tom observed how the paper shook and rustled in the tremor of excitement that shook his hand. He raised the paper to the focus of his spectacles and began to read again. "'Mark 40, 72, 91—'"

"Mark?" cried out Tom, almost screaming. "Why, that must mean the stake yonder; that must be the mark." And he pointed to the oaken stick with its red tip blazing against the white shimmer of sand behind it.

"And the 40 and 72 and 91," cried the old gentleman, in a voice equally shrill—"why, that must mean the number of steps the pirate was counting when you heard him."

"To be sure that's what they meant!" cried Tom Chist. "That is it, and it can be nothing else. Oh, come, sir—come, sir; let us make haste and find it!"

"Stay! stay!" said the good gentleman, holding up his hand; and again Tom Chist noticed how it trembled and shook. His voice was steady enough, though very hoarse, but his hand shook and trembled as though with a palsy. "Stay! stay! First of all, we must follow these measurements. And 'tis a marvelous thing," he croaked, after a little pause, "how this paper ever came to be here."

"Maybe it was blown here by the storm," suggested Tom Chist.

"Like enough; like enough," said Parson Jones. "Like enough, after the wretches had buried the chest and killed the poor black man, they were so buffeted and bowsed about by the storm that it was shook out of the man's pocket, and thus blew away from him without his knowing aught of it."

"But let us find the box!" cried out Tom Chist, flaming with his excitement.

"Aye, aye," said the good man; "only stay a little, my boy, until we make sure what we're about. I've got my pocket compass here, but we must have something to measure off the feet when we have found the peg. You run across to Tom Brooke's house and fetch that measuring rod he used to lay out his new byre. While you're gone I'll pace off the distance marked on the paper with my pocket compass here."

6

Tom Chist was gone for almost an hour, though he ran nearly all the way and back, upborne as on the wings of the wind. When he returned, panting, Parson Jones was nowhere to be seen, but Tom saw his footsteps leading away inland, and he followed the scuffling marks in the smooth surface across the sand humps and down into the hollows, and by and by found the good gentleman in a spot he at once knew as soon as he laid his eyes upon it.

It was the open space where the pirates had driven their first peg, and where Tom Chist had afterward seen them kill the poor black man. Tom Chist gazed around as though expecting to see some sign of the tragedy, but the space was as smooth and as undisturbed as a floor, excepting where, midway across it, Parson Jones, who was now stooping over something on the ground, had trampled it all around about.

When Tom Chist saw him he was still bending over, scraping away from something he had found.

It was the first peg!

Inside of half an hour they had found the second and third pegs, and Tom Chist stripped off his coat, and began digging like mad down into the sand, Parson Jones standing over him watching him. The sun was sloping well toward the west when the blade of Tom Chist's spade struck upon something hard.

If it had been his own heart that he had hit in the sand his breast could hardly have thrilled more sharply.

It was the treasure box!

Parson Jones himself leaped down into the hole, and began scraping away the sand with his hands as though he had gone crazy. At last, with some difficulty, they tugged and hauled the chest up out of the sand to the surface, where it lay covered all over with the grit that clung to it. It was securely locked and fastened with a padlock, and it took a goood many blows with the blade of the spade to burst the bolt. Parson Jones himself lifted the lid. Tom Chist leaned forward and gazed down into the open box. He would not have been surprised to have seen it filled full of yellow gold and bright jewels. It was filled half full of books and papers, and half full of canvas bags tied safely and securely around and around with cords of string.

Parson Jones lifted out one of the bags, and it jingled as he did so. It was full of money.

125

He cut the string, and with trembling, shaking hands handed the bag to Tom, who, in an ecstasy of wonder and dizzy with delight, poured out with swimming sight upon the coat spread on the ground a cataract of shining silver money that rang and twinkled and jingled as it fell in a shining heap upon the coarse cloth.

Parson Jones held up both hands into the air, and Tom stared at what he saw, wondering whether it was all so, and whether he was really awake. It seemed to him as though he was in a dream.

There were two-and-twenty bags in all in the chest: ten of them full of silver money, eight of them full of gold money, three of them full of gold dust, and one small bag with jewels wrapped up in wad cotton and paper.

" 'Tis enough," cried out Parson Jones, "to make us both rich men as long as we live."

The burning summer sun, though sloping in the sky, beat down upon them as hot as fire; but neither of them noticed it. Neither did they notice hunger nor thirst nor fatigue, but sat there as though in a trance, with the bags of money scattered on the sand around them, a great pile of money heaped upon the coat, and the open chest beside them. It was an hour of sundown before Parson Jones had begun fairly to examine the books and papers in the chest.

Of the three books, two were evidently log books of the pirates who had been lying off the mouth of the Delaware Bay all this time. The other book was written in Spanish, and was evidently the log book of some captured prize.

It was then, sitting there upon the sand, the good old gentleman reading in his high, cracking voice, that they first learned from the bloody records in those two books who it was who had been lying inside the Cape all this time, and that it was the famous Captain Kidd. Every now and then the reverend gentleman would stop to exclaim, "Oh, the bloody wretch!" or, "Oh, the desperate, cruel villains!" and then would go on reading again a scrap here and a scrap there.

And all the while Tom Chist sat and listened, every now and then reaching out furtively and touching the heap of money still lying upon the coat.

One might be inclined to wonder why Captain Kidd had kept those bloody records. He had probably laid them away because they so incriminated many of the great people of the colony of New York that, with the books in evidence, it would have been impossible to bring the pirate to justice without dragging a dozen or more fine gentlemen into the dock along with him. If he could have kept them in his own possession they would doubtless have been a great weapon of defense to protect him from the gallows. Indeed, when Captain Kidd was finally brought to conviction and hung, he was not accused of his piracies, but of striking a mutinous seaman upon the head with a bucket and accidentally killing him. The authorities did not dare try him for piracy. He was really hung because he was pirate, and we know that it was the log books that Tom Chist brought to New York that did the business for him; he was accused and convicted of manslaughter for killing of his own ship carpenter with a bucket.

So Parson Jones, sitting there in the slanting light, read through these terrible records of piracy, and Tom, with a pile of gold and silver money beside him, sat and listened to him.

What a spectacle, if anyone had come upon them! But they were alone, with the vast arch of sky empty above them and the wide white stretch of sand a desert around them. The sun sank lower and lower, until there was only time to glance through the other papers in the chest.

They were nearly all goldsmiths' bills of exchange drawn in favor of certain of the most prominent merchants of New York.

Parson Jones, as he read over the names, knew of nearly all the gentlemen by hearsay. Aye, here was this gentleman; he thought that name would be among 'em. What? Here is Mr. So-and-so. Well, if all they say is true, the villain has robbed one of own best friends. "I wonder," he said, "why the wretch should have hidden these papers so carefully away with the other treasures, for they could do him no good?" Then, answering his own question: "Like enough because these will give him a hold over the gentlemen to whom they are drawn so that he can make a good bargain for his own neck before he gives the bills back to their owners. I tell you what it is, Tom," he continued, "it is you yourself shall go to New York and bargain for the return of these papers. 'Twill be as good as another fortune to you."

The majority of the bills were drawn in favor of one Richard Chillingsworth, Esquire. "And he is," said Parson Jones, "one of the richest men in the province of New York. You shall go to him with the news of what we have found."

"When shall I go?" said Tom Chist.

"You shall go upon the very first boat we can catch," said the parson. He had turned, still holding the bills in his hand, and was now fingering over the pile of money that yet lay tumbled out upon the coat. "I wonder, Tom," said he, "if you could spare me a score or so of these doubloons?"

"You shall have fifty score, if you choose," said Tom, bursting with gratitude and with generosity in his newly found treasure.

"You are as fine a lad as ever I saw, Tom," said the parson, "and I'll thank you to the last day of my life."

Tom scooped up a double handful of silver money. "Take it, sir," he said, "and you may have as much more as you want of it."

He poured it into the dish that the good man made of his

hands, and the parson made a motion as though to empty it into his pocket. Then he stopped, as though a sudden doubt had occurred to him. "I don't know that 'tis fit for me to take this pirate money, after all," he said.

"But you are welcome to it," said Tom.

Still the parson hesitated. "Nay," he burst out, "I'll not take it; 'tis blood money." And as he spoke he chucked the whole double handful into the now empty chest, then arose and dusted the sand from his breeches. Then, with a great deal of bustling energy, he helped to tie the bags again and put them all back into the chest.

They reburied the chest in the place whence they had taken it, and then the parson folded the precious paper of directions, placed it carefully in his wallet, and his wallet in his pocket. "Tom," he said, for the twentieth time, "your fortune has been made this day."

And Tom Chist, as he rattled in his breeches pocket the half dozen doubloons he had kept out of his treasure, felt that what his friend had said was true.

As the two went back homeward across the level space of sand Tom Chist suddenly stopped stock-still and stood looking about him. " 'Twas just here," he said, digging his heel down into the sand, "that they killed the poor black man."

"And here he lies buried for all time," said Parson Jones; and as he spoke he dug his cane down into the sand. Tom Chist shuddered. He would not have been surprised if the ferrule of the cane had struck something soft beneath that level surface. But it did not, nor was any sign of that tragedy ever seen again. For, whether the pirates had carried away what they had done and buried it elsewhere, or whether the storm in blowing the sand had completely leveled off and hidden all sign of that tragedy where it was enacted, certain it is that it never came to sight again—at least as far as Tom Chist and the Rev. Hilary Jones ever knew.

7

This is the story of the treasure box. All that remains now is to conclude the story of Tom Chist, and to tell of what came of him in the end.

He did not go back again to live with old Matt Abrahamson. Parson Jones had now taken charge of him and his fortunes, and Tom did not have to go back to the fisherman's hut.

Old Abrahamson talked a great deal about it, and would come in his cups and harangue good Parson Jones, making a vast protestation of what he would do to Tom—if he ever caught him—for running away. But Tom on all these occasions kept carefully out of his way, and nothing came of the old man's threatenings.

Tom used to go over to see his foster mother now and then, but always when the old man was from home. And Molly Abrahamson used to warn him to keep out of her father's way. "He's in as vile a humor as ever I see, Tom," she said; "he sits sulking all day long, and 'tis my belief he'd kill ye if he caught ye."

Of course Tom said nothing, even to her, about the treasure, and he and the reverend gentleman kept the knowledge thereof to themselves. About three weeks later Parson Jones managed to get him shipped aboard of a vessel bound for New York town, and a few days later Tom Chist landed at that place. He had never been in such a town before, and he could not sufficiently wonder and marvel at the number of brick houses, at the multitude of people coming and going along the fine, hard earthen sidewalk, at the shops and the stores where goods hung in the windows, and, most of all, the fortifications and the

130

battery at the point, at the rows of threatening cannon, and at the scarlet-coated sentries pacing up and down the ramparts. All this was very wonderful, and so were the clustered boats riding at anchor in the harbor. It was like a new world, so different was it from the sand hills and the sedgy levels of Henlopen.

Tom Chist took up his lodgings at a coffee house near to the town hall, and thence he sent by the postboy a letter written by Parson Jones to Master Chillingsworth. In a little while the boy returned with a message, asking Tom to come up to Mr. Chillingsworth's house that afternoon at two o'clock.

Tom went thither with a great deal of trepidation, and his heart fell away altogether when he found it a fine, grand brick house, three stories high, and with wrought-iron letters across the front.

The counting house was in the same building; but Tom, because of Mr. Jones's letter, was conducted directly into the parlor, where the great rich man was awaiting his coming. He was sitting in a leather-covered armchair, smoking a pipe of tobacco, and with a bottle of fine old Madeira close to his elbow.

Tom had not had a chance to buy a new suit of clothes yet, and so he cut no very fine figure in the rough dress he had brought with him from Henlopen. Nor did Mr. Chillingsworth seem to think very highly of his appearance, for he sat looking sideways at Tom as he smoked.

"Well, my lad," he said, "and what is this great thing you have to tell me that is so mightily wonderful? I got what's-his-name—Mr. Jones's—letter, and now I am ready to hear what you have to say."

But if he thought but little of his visitor's appearance at first, he soon changed his sentiments toward him, for Tom had not spoken twenty words when Mr. Chillingsworth's whole

131

aspect changed. He straightened himself up in his seat, laid aside his pipe, pushed away his glass of Madeira, and bade Tom take a chair.

He listened without a word as Tom Chist told of the buried treasure, of how he had seen the poor negro murdered, and of how he and Parson Jones had recovered the chest again. Only once did Mr. Chillingsworth interrupt the narrative. "And to think," he cried, "that the villain this very day walks about New York town as though he were an honest man, ruffling it with the best of us! But if we can only get hold of these log books you speak of. Go on; tell me more of this."

When Tom Chist's narrative was ended, Mr. Chillingsworth's bearing was as different as daylight is from dark. He asked a thousand questions, all in the most polite and gracious tone imaginable, and not only urged a glass of his fine old Madeira upon Tom, but asked him to stay to supper. There was nobody to be there, he said, but his wife and daughter.

Tom, all in a panic at the very thought of the two ladies, sturdily refused to stay even for the dish of tea Mr. Chillingsworth offered him.

He did not know that he was destined to stay there as long as he should live.

"And now," said Mr. Chillingsworth, "tell me about yourself."

"I have nothing to tell, Your Honor," said Tom, "except that I was washed up out of the sea."

"Washed up out of the sea!" exclaimed Mr. Chillingsworth. "Why, how was that? Come, begin at the beginning, and tell me all."

Thereupon Tom Chist did as he was bidden, beginning at the very beginning and telling everything just as Molly Abrahamson had often told it to him. As he continued, Mr. Chillingsworth's interest changed into an appearance of stronger and stronger excitement. Suddenly he jumped up out of his chair and began to walk up and down the room.

"Stop! stop!" he cried out at last, in the midst of something Tom was saying. "Stop! stop! Tell me; do you know the name of the vessel that was wrecked, and from which you were washed ashore?"

"I've heard it said," said Tom Chist, "'twas the *Bristol Merchant*."

"I knew it! I knew it!" exclaimed the great man, in a loud voice, flinging his hands up into the air. "I felt it was so the moment you began the story. But tell me this, was there nothing found with you with a mark or a name upon it?"

"There was a kerchief," said Tom, "marked with a T and a C."

"Theodosia Chillingsworth!" cried out the merchant. "I knew it! I knew it! Heavens! to think of anything so wonderful happening as this! Boy! boy! dost thou know who thou art? Thou art my own brother's son. His name was Oliver Chillingsworth, and he was my partner in business, and thou art his son." Then he ran out into the entryway, shouting and calling for his wife and daughter to come.

So Tom Chist—or Thomas Chillingsworth, as he now was to be called—did stay to supper, after all.

This is the story, and I hope you may like it. For Tom Chist became rich and great, as was to be supposed, and he married his pretty cousin Theodosia (who had been named for his own mother, drowned in the *Bristol Merchant*).

He did not forget his friends, but had Parson Jones brought to New York to live.

As to Molly and Matt Abrahamson, they both enjoyed a pension of ten pounds a year for as long as they lived; for now that all was well with him, Tom bore no grudge against the old fisherman for all the drubbings he had suffered.

The treasure box was brought on to New York, and if Tom Chist did not get all the money there was in it (as Parson Jones had opined he would) he got at least a good big lump of it.

And it is my belief that those log books did more to get Captain Kidd arrested in Boston town and hanged in London than anything else that was brought up against him.

V

FROM "JACK BALLISTER'S FORTUNES"

1

E, of these times, protected as we are by the laws and by the number of people about us, can hardly comprehend such a life as that of the American colonies in the early part of the eighteenth century, when it was possible for a pirate like Capt. Teach, known as Blackbeard, to exist, and for the governor and the secretary of the province in which he lived perhaps to share his plunder, and to shelter and to protect him against the law.

At that time the American colonists were in general a rough, rugged people, knowing nothing of the finer things of life. They lived mostly in little settlements, separated by long distances from one another, so that they could neither make nor enforce laws to protect themselves. Each man or little group of men had to depend upon his or their own strength to keep what belonged to them, and to prevent fierce men or groups of men from seizing what did not belong to them.

It is the natural disposition of everyone to get all that he can. Little children, for instance, always try to take away from others that which they want, and to keep it for their own. It is only by constant teaching that they learn that they must not do so; that they must not take by force what does not belong to them. So it is only by teaching and training that people learn to be honest and not to take what is not theirs. When this teaching is not sufficient to make a man learn to be honest, or when there is something in the man's nature that makes him not able to learn, then he only lacks the opportunity to seize upon the things he wants, just as he would do if he were a little child.

In the colonies at that time, as was just said, men were too few and scattered to protect themselves against those who had made up their minds to take by force that which they wanted, and so it was that men lived an unrestrained and lawless life, such as we of these times of better government can hardly comprehend.

The usual means of commerce between province and province was by water in coasting vessels. These coasting vessels were so defenseless, and the different colonial governments were so ill able to protect them, that those who chose to rob them could do it almost without danger to themselves.

So it was that all the western world was, in those days, infested with armed bands of cruising freebooters or pirates, who used to stop merchant vessels and take from them what they chose.

Each province in those days was ruled over by a royal governor appointed by the king. Each governor, at one time, was free to do almost as he pleased in his own province. He was accountable only to the king and his government, and England was so distant that he was really responsible almost to nobody but himself.

The governors were naturally just as desirous to get rich

quickly, just as desirous of getting all that they could for themselves, as was anybody else—only they had been taught and
had been able to learn that is was not right to be an actual
pirate or robber. They wanted to be rich easily and quickly, but
the desire was not strong enough to lead them to dishonor
themselves in their own opinion and in the opinion of others
by gratifying their selfishness. They would even have stopped
the pirates from doing what they did if they could, but their
provincial governments were too weak to prevent the freebooters from robbing merchant vessels, or to punish them when
they came ashore. The provinces had no navies, and they really
had no armies; neither were there enough people living within
the community to enforce the laws against those stronger and
fiercer men who were not honest.

After the things the pirates seized from merchant vessels
were once stolen they were altogether lost. Almost never did
any owner apply for them, for it would be useless to do so.
The stolen goods and merchandise lay in the storehouses of the
pirates, seemingly without any owner excepting the pirates
themselves.

The governors and the secretaries of the colonies would not
dishonor themselves by pirating upon merchant vessels, but it
did not seem so wicked after the goods were stolen—and so
altogether lost—to take a part of that which seemed to have
no owner.

A child is taught that is a very wicked thing to take, for
instance, by force, a lump of sugar from another child; but
when a wicked child has seized the sugar from another and
taken it around the corner, and that other child from whom he
has seized it has gone home crying, it does not seem so wicked
for the third child to take a bite of the sugar when it is offered
to him, even if he thinks it has been taken from some one else.

It was just so, no doubt, that it did not seem so wicked to

137

Governor Eden and Secretary Knight of North Carolina, or to Governor Fletcher of New York, or to other colonial governors, to take a part of the booty that the pirates, such as Blackbeard, had stolen. It did not even seem very wicked to compel such pirates to give up a part of what was not theirs, and which seemed to have no owner.

In Governor Eden's time, however, the colonies had begun to be more thickly peopled, and the laws had gradually become stronger and stronger to protect men in the possession of what was theirs. Governor Eden was the last of the colonial governors who had dealings with the pirates, and Blackbeard was almost the last of the pirates who, with his banded men, was savage and powerful enough to come and go as he chose among the people whom he plundered.

Virginia, at that time, was the greatest and the richest of all the American colonies, and upon the farther side of North Carolina was the province of South Carolina, also strong and rich. It was these two colonies that suffered the most from Blackbeard, and it began to be that the honest men that lived in them could endure no longer to be plundered.

The merchants and traders and others who suffered cried out loudly for protection, so loudly that the governors of these provinces could not help hearing them.

Governor Eden was petitioned to act against the pirates, but he would do nothing, for he felt very friendly toward Blackbeard—just as a child who has had a taste of the stolen sugar feels friendly toward the child who gives it to him.

At last, when Blackbeard sailed up into the very heart of Virginia, and seized upon and carried away the daughter of that colony's foremost people, the governor of Virginia, finding that the governor of North Carolina would do nothing to punish the outrage, took the matter into his own hands and issued a proclamation offering a reward of one hundred pounds for

Who Shall Be Captain?

Blackbeard, alive or dead, and different sums for the other pirates who where his followers.

Governor Spottiswood had the right to issue the proclamation, but he had no right to commission Lieutenant Maynard, as he did, to take down an armed force into the neighboring province and to attack the pirates in the waters of the North Carolina sounds. It was all a part of the rude and lawless condition of the colonies at the time that such a thing could have been done.

The governor's proclamation against the pirates was issued upon the eleventh day of November. It was read in the churches the Sunday following and was posted upon the doors of all the government custom offices in lower Virginia. Lieutenant Maynard, in the boats that Colonel Parker had already fitted out to go against the pirates, set sail upon the seventeenth of the month for Ocracoke. Five days later the battle was fought.

Blackbeard's sloop was lying inside of Ocracoke Inlet among the shoals and sand bars when he first heard of Governer Spottiswood's proclamation.

There had been a storm, and a good many vessels had run into the inlet for shelter. Blackbeard knew nearly all of the Captains of these vessels, and it was from them that he first heard of the proclamation.

He had gone aboard one of the vessels—a coaster from Boston. The wind was still blowing pretty hard from the southeast. There were maybe a dozen vessels lying within the inlet at that time, and the captain of one of them was paying the Boston skipper a visit when Blackbeard came aboard. The two captains had been talking together. They instantly ceased when the pirate came down into the cabin, but he had heard enough of their conversation to catch its drift. "Why d'ye stop?"

139

he said. "I heard what you said. Well, what then? D'ye think I mind it at all? Spottiswood is going to send his bullies down here after me. That's what you were saying. Well, what then? You don't think I'm afraid of his bullies, do you?"

"Why, no, captain, I didn't say you was afraid," said the visiting captain.

"And what right has he got to send down here against me in North Carolina, I should like to ask you?"

"He's got none at all," said the Boston captain, soothingly. "Won't you take a taste of Hollands, Captain?"

"He's no more right to come blustering down here into Governor Eden's province than I have to come aboard of your schooner here, Tom Burley, and to carry off two or three kegs of this prime Hollands for my own drinking."

Captain Burley—the Boston man—laughed a loud, forced laugh. "Why, Captain," he said, "as for two or three kegs of Hollands, you won't find that aboard. But if you'd like to have a keg of it for your own drinking, I'll send it to you and be glad enough to do so for old acquaintance' sake."

"But I tell you what 'tis, Captain," said the visiting skipper to Blackbeard, "they're determined and set against you this time. I tell you, Captain, Governor Spottiswood hath issued a hot proclamation against you, and 't hath been read out in all the churches. I myself saw it posted in Yorktown upon the customhouse door and read it there myself. The governor offers one hundred pounds for you, and fifty pounds for your officers, and twenty pounds each for your men."

"Well, then," said Blackbeard, holding up his glass, "here, I wish 'em good luck, and when they get their hundred pounds for me they'll be in a poor way to spend it. As for the Hollands," said he, turning to Captain Burley, "I know what you've got aboard here and what you haven't. D'ye suppose ye can blind me? Very well, you send over two kegs, and I'll

140

let you go without search." The two captains were very silent. "As for that Lieutenant Maynard you're all talking about," said Blackbeard, "why, I know him very well. He was the one who was so busy with the pirates down Madagascar way. I believe you'd all like to see him blow me out of the water, but he can't do it. There's nobody in His Majesty's service I'd rather meet than Lieutenant Maynard. I'd teach him prettly briskly that North Carolina isn't Madagascar."

On the evening of the twenty-second the two vessels under command of Lieutenant Maynard came into the mouth of Ocracoke Inlet and there dropped anchor. Meantime the weather had cleared, and all the vessels but one had gone from the inlet. The one vessel that remained was a New Yorker. It had been there over a night and a day, and the captain and Blackbeard had become very good friends.

The same night that Maynard came into the inlet a wedding was held on the shore. A number of men and women came up the beach in oxcarts and sledges; others had come in boats from more distant points and across the water.

The captain of the New Yorker and Blackbeard went ashore together a little after dark. The New Yorker had been aboard of the pirate's sloop for all the latter part of the afternoon, and he and Blackbeard had been drinking together in the cabin. The New York man was now a little tipsy, and he laughed and talked foolishly as he and Blackbeard were rowed ashore. The pirate sat grim and silent.

It was nearly dark when they stepped ashore on the beach. The New York captain stumbled and fell headlong, rolling over and over, and the crew of the boat burst out laughing.

The people had already begun to dance in an open shed fronting upon the shore. There were fires of pine knots in front of the building, lighting up the interior with a red glare. A negro was playing a fiddle somewhere inside, and the shed was filled with a crowd of grotesque dancing figures—men and women. Now and then they called with loud voices as they danced, and the squeaking of the fiddle sounded incessantly through the noise of outcries and the stamp and shuffling of feet.

Captain Teach and the New York captain stood looking on. The New York man had tilted himself against a post and stood there holding one arm around it, supporting himself. He waved the other hand foolishly in time to the music, now and then snapping his thumb and finger.

The young woman who had just been married approached the two. She had been dancing, and she was warm and red, her hair blowzed about her head. "Hi, Captain, won't you dance with me?" she said to Blackbeard.

Blackbeard stared at her. "Who be you?" he said.

She burst out laughing. "You look as if you'd eat a body," she cried.

Blackbeard's face gradually relaxed. "Why, to be sure, you're a brazen one, for all the world," he said. "Well, I'll dance with you, that I will. I'll dance the heart out of you."

He pushed forward, thrusting aside with his elbow the newly made husband. The man, who saw that Blackbeard had been drinking, burst out laughing, and the other men and women who had been standing around drew away, so that in a little while the floor was pretty well cleared. One could see the negro now; he sat on a barrel at the end of the room. He grinned with his white teeth and, without stopping in his fiddling, scraped his bow harshly across the strings, and then instantly changed the tune to a lively jig. Blackbeard jumped up into the air and clapped his heels together, giving, as he did so, a sharp, short yell. Then he began instantly dancing grotesquely and violently. The woman danced opposite to him, this way and that, with her knuckles on her hips. Everybody burst out laughing at Blackbeard's grotesque antics. They lauged again and again, clapping their hands, and the negro scraped away on his fiddle like fury. The woman's hair came tumbling down her back. She tucked it back, laughing and panting, and the sweat ran down her face. She danced and danced. At last she burst out laughing and stopped, panting. Blackbeard again jumped up in the air and clapped his heels. Again he yelled, and as he did so, he struck his heels upon the floor and spun around. Once more everybody burst out laughing, clapping their hands, and the negro stopped fiddling.

Near by was a shanty or cabin where they were selling spirits, and by and by Blackbeard went there with the New York captain, and presently they began drinking again. "Hi, Captain!" called one of the men, "Maynard's out yonder in the inlet. Jack Bishop's just come across from t'other side. He says Mr. Maynard hailed him and asked for a pilot to fetch him in."

"Well, here's luck to him, and he can't come in quick enough for me!" cried out Blackbeard in his hoarse, husky voice.

"Well, Captain," called a voice, "will ye fight him tomorrow?"

"Aye," shouted the pirate, "if he can get in to me, I'll try to give 'em what they seek, and all they want of it into the bargain. As for a pilot, I tell ye what 'tis—if any man hereabouts goes out there to pilot that villain in 'twill be the worst day's work he ever did in all of his life. 'Twont be fit for him to live in these parts of America if I am living here at the same time." There was a burst of laughter.

"Give us a toast, Captain! Give us something to drink to! Aye, Captain, a toast! A toast!" a half dozen voices were calling out at the same time.

"Well," cried out the pirate captain, "here's to a good, hot fight to-morrow, and the best dog on top! 'Twill be, Bang! bang!—this way!"

He began pulling a pistol out of his pocket, but it stuck in the lining, and he struggled and tugged at it. The men ducked and scrambled away from before him, and then the next moment he had the pistol out of his pocket. He swung it around and around. There was perfect silence. Suddenly there was a flash and a stunning report, and instantly a crash and tinkle of broken glass. One of the men cried out, and began picking and jerking at the back of his neck. "He's broken that bottle all down my neck," he called out.

"That's the way 'twill be," said Blackbeard.

"Lookee," said the owner of the place, "I won't serve out another drop if 'tis going to be like that. If there's any more trouble I'll blow out the lantern."

The sound of the squeaking and scraping of the fiddle and the shouts and the scuffling feet still came from the shed where the dancing was going on.

"Suppose you get your dose to-morrow, Captain," some one called out, "what then?"

"Why, if I do," said Blackbeard, "I get it, and that's all there is of it."

"Your wife'll be a rich widdy then, won't she?" cried one of the men; and there was a burst of laughter.

"Why," said the New York captain,—"why, has a—a bloody p-pirate like you a wife then—a—like any honest man?"

"She'll be no richer than she is now," said Blackbeard.

"She knows where you've hid your money, anyways. Don't she, Captain?" called out a voice.

"The divil knows where I've hid my money," said Blackbeard, "and I know where I've hid it; and the longest liver of the twain will git it all. And that's all there is of it."

144

The gray of early day was beginning to show in the east when Blackbeard and the New York captain came down to the landing together. The New York captain swayed and toppled this way and that as he walked, now falling against Blackbeard, and now staggering away from him.

2

Early in the morning—perhaps eight o'clock—Lieutenant Maynard sent a boat from the schooner over to the settlement, which lay some four or five miles distant. A number of men stood lounging on the landing, watching the approach of the boat. The men rowed close up to the wharf, and there lay upon their oars, while the boatswain of the schooner, who was in command of the boat, stood up and asked if there was any man there who could pilot them over the shoals.

Nobody answered, but all stared stupidly at him. After a while one of the men at last took his pipe out of his mouth. "There ben't any pilot here, master," said he; "we ben't pilots."

"Why, what a story you do tell!" roared the boatswain. "D'ye suppose I've never been down here before, not to know that every man about here knows the passes of the shoals?"

The fellow still held his pipe in his hand. He looked at another one of the men. "Do you know the passes in over the shoals, Jem?" said he.

The man to whom he spoke was a young fellow with long, shaggy, sunburnt hair hanging over his eyes in an unkempt mass. He shook his head, grunting, "No—I don't know naught about t' shoals."

"'Tis Lieutenant Maynard of His Majesty's navy in command of them vessels out there," said the boatswain. "He'll give any man five pound to pilot him in." The men on the wharf looked at one another, but still no one spoke, and the ·

145

boatswain stood looking at them. He saw that they did not choose to answer him. "Why," he said, "I believe you've not got right wits—that's what I believe is the matter with you. Pull me up to the landing, men, and I'll go ashore and see if I can find anybody that's willing to make five pound for such a little bit of piloting as that."

After the boatswain had gone ashore the loungers still stood on the wharf, looking down into the boat, and began talking to one another for the men below to hear them. "They're coming in," said one, "to blow poor Blackbeard out of the water." "Aye," said another, "he's so peaceable, too, he is; he'll just lay still and let 'em blow and blow, he will." "There's a young fellow there," said another of the men; "he don't look fit to die yet, he don't. Why, I wouldn't be in his place for a thousand pound." "I do suppose Blackbeard's so afraid he don't know how to see," said the first speaker.

At last one of the men in the boat spoke up. "Maybe he don't know how to see," said he, "but maybe we'll blow some daylight into him afore we get through with him."

Some more of the settlers had come out from the shore to the end of the wharf, and there was now quite a crowd gathering there, all looking at the men in the boat. "What do them Virginny 'baccy-eaters do down here in Caroliny, anyway?" said one of the newcomers. "They've got no call to be down here in North Caroliny waters."

"Maybe you can keep us away from coming, and maybe you can't," said a voice from the boat.

"Why," answered the man on the wharf, "we could keep you away easy enough, but you ben't worth the trouble, and that's the truth."

There was a heavy iron bolt lying near the edge of the landing. One of the men upon the wharf slyly thrust it out

146

with the end of his foot. It hung for a moment and then fell into the boat below with a crash. "What d'ye mean by that?" roared the man in charge of the boat. "What d'ye mean, ye villains? D'ye mean to stave a hole in us?"

"Why," said the man who had pushed it, "you saw 'twasn't done a purpose, didn't you?"

"Well, you try it again, and somebody'll get hurt," said the man in the boat, showing the butt end of his pistol.

The men on the wharf began laughing. Just then the boatswain came down from the settlement again, and out along the landing. The threatened turbulence quieted as he approached, and the crowd moved sullenly aside to let him pass. He did not bring any pilot with him, and he jumped down into the stern of the boat, saying, briefly, "Push off." The crowd of loungers stood looking after them as they rowed away, and when the boat was some distance from the landing they burst out into a volley of derisive yells. "The villains!" said the boatswain, "they are all in league together. They wouldn't even let me go up into the settlement to look for a pilot."

The lieutenant and his sailing master stood watching the boat as it approached. "Couldn't you, then, get a pilot, Baldwin?" said Mr. Maynard, as the boatswain scrambled aboard.

"No, I couldn't sir," said the man. "Either they're all banded together, or else they're all afraid of the villains. They wouldn't even let me go up into the settlement to find one."

"Well, then," said Mr. Maynard, "we'll make shift to work in as best we may by ourselves. 'Twill be high tide against one o'clock. We'll run in then with sail as far as we can, and then we'll send you ahead with the boat to sound for a pass, and we'll follow with the sweeps. You know the waters pretty well, you say."

147

"They were saying ashore that the villain hath forty men aboard," said the boatswain.[1]

Lieutenant Maynard's force consisted of thirty-five men in the schooner and twenty-five men in the sloop. He carried neither cannons nor carronades, and neither of his vessels was very well fitted for the purpose for which they were designed. The schooner, which he himself commanded, offered almost no protection to the crew. The rail was not more than a foot high in the waist, and the men on the deck were almost entirely exposed. The rail of the sloop was perhaps a little higher, but it, too, was hardly better adapted for fighting. Indeed, the lieutenant depended more upon the moral force of official authority to overawe the pirates than upon any real force of arms or men. He never believed, until the very last moment, that the pirates would show any real fight. It is very possible that they might not have done so had they not thought that the lieutenant had actually no legal right supporting him in his attack upon them in North Carolina waters.

It was about noon when anchor was hoisted, and, with the schooner leading, both vessels ran slowly in before a light wind that had begun to blow toward midday. In each vessel a man stood in the bows, sounding continually with lead and line. As they slowly opened up the harbor within the inlet, they could see the pirate sloop lying about three miles away. There was a boat just putting off from it to the shore.

The lieutenant and his sailing master stood together on the roof of the cabin deckhouse. The sailing master held a glass to his eye. "She carries a long gun, sir," he said, and four carronades. She'll be hard to beat, sir, I do suppose, armed as we are with only light arms for close fighting."

The lieutenant laughed. "Why, Brookes," he said, "you seem

---

[1] The pirate captain had really only twenty-five men aboard of his sloop at the time of the battle.

He Led Jack Up to a Man Who Sat Upon a Barrel

to think forever of these men showing fight. You don't know them as I know them. They have a deal of bluster and make a deal of noise, but when you seize them and hold them with a strong hand, there's naught of fight left in them. 'Tis like enough there'll not be so much as a musket fired to-day. I've had to do with 'em often enough before to know my gentlemen well by this time." Nor, as was said, was it until the very last that the lieutenant could be brought to believe that the pirates had any stomach for a fight.

The two vessels had reached perhaps within a mile of the pirate sloop before they found the water too shoal to venture any farther with the sail. It was then that the boat was lowered as the lieutenant had planned, and the boatswain went ahead to sound, the two vessels, with their sail still hoisted but empty of wind, pulling in after with sweeps.

The pirate had also hoisted sail, but lay as though waiting for the approach of the schooner and the sloop.

The boat in which the boatswain was sounding had run in a considerable distance ahead of the two vessels, which were gradually creeping up with the sweeps until they had reached to within less than half a mile of the pirates—the boat with the boatswain maybe a quarter of a mile closer. Suddenly there was a puff of smoke from the pirate sloop, and then another and another, and the next moment there came the three reports of muskets up the wind.

"By zounds!" said the lieutenant. "I do believe they're firing on the boat!" And then he saw the boat turn and begin pulling toward them.

The boat with the boatswain aboard came rowing rapidly. Again there were three or four puffs of smoke and three or four subsequent reports from the distant vessel. Then, in a little while, the boat was alongside, and the boatswain came scrambling aboard. "Never mind hoisting the boat," said the lieutenant; "we'll just take her in tow. Come aboard as quick as you can." Then, turning to the sailing master, "Well, Brookes, you'll have to do the best you can to get in over the shoals under half sail."

"But, sir," said the master, "we'll be sure to run aground."

"Very well, sir," said the lieutenant, "you heard my orders. If we run aground we run aground, and that's all there is of it."

"I sounded as far as maybe a little over a fathom," said the mate, "but the villains would let me go no nearer. I think I was in the channel, though. 'Tis more open inside, as I mind me of it. There's a kind of a hole there, and if we get in over the shoals just beyond where I was we'll be all right."

"Very well, then, you take the wheel, Baldwin," said the lieutenant, "and do the best you can for us."

Lieutenant Maynard stood looking out forward at the pirate vessel, which they were now steadily nearing under half sail. He could see that there were signs of bustle aboard and of men running around upon the deck. Then he walked aft and around the cabin. The sloop was some distance astern. It appeared to have run aground, and they were trying to push it off with the sweeps. The lieutenant looked down into the water over the stern, and saw that the schooner was already raising the mud in her wake. Then he went forward along the deck. His men were crouching down along by the low rail, and there was a tense quietness of expectation about them. The lieutenant looked them over as he passed them. "Johnson," he said, "do you take the lead and line and go forward and sound a bit." Then to the others: "Now, my men, the moment we run her aboard, you get aboard of her as quick as you can, do you understand? Don't wait for the sloop or think about her, but just see that the grappling irons are fast, and then get aboard. If any man offers to resist you, shoot him down. Are you ready, Mr. Cringle?"

"Aye, aye, sir," said the gunner.

"Very well, then, be ready, men; we'll be aboard 'em in a minute or two."

"There's less than a fathom of water here, sir," sang out Johnson from the bows. As he spoke there was a sudden soft jar and jerk, then the schooner was still. They were aground. "Push her off to the lee there! Let go your sheets!" roared the boatswain from the wheel. "Push her off to the lee." He spun the wheel around as he spoke. A half dozen men sprang up, seized the sweeps, and plunged them into the water. Others ran to help them, but the sweeps only sank into the mud without moving the schooner. The sails had fallen off and they were flapping and thumping and clapping in the wind. Others of the crew had scrambled to their feet and ran to help those at the sweeps. The lieutenant had walked quickly aft again. They were very close now to the pirate sloop, and suddenly some one hailed him from aboard of her. When he turned he saw that there was a man standing up on the rail of the pirate sloop, holding by the back stays. "Who are you?" he called, from the distance, "and whence come you? What do you seek here? What d'ye mean, coming down on us this way?"

The lieutenant heard somebody say, "That's Blackbeard hisself." And he looked with great interest at the distant figure.

The pirate stood out boldly against the cloudy sky. Somebody seemed to speak to him from behind. He turned his head and then he turned round again. "We're only peaceful merchantmen!" he called out. "What authority have you got to come down upon us this way? If you'll come aboard I'll show you my papers and that we're only peaceful merchantmen."

"The villains!" said the lieutenant to the master, who stood beside him. "They're peaceful merchantmen, are they! They look like peaceful merchantmen, with four carronades and a long gun aboard!" Then he called out across the water, "I'll

151

come aboard with my schooner as soon as I can push her off here."

"If you undertake to come aboard of me," called the pirate, "I'll shoot into you. You've got no authority to board me, and I won't have you do it. If you undertake it 'twill be at your own risk, for I'll neither ask quarter of you nor give none."

"Very well," said the lieutenant, "if you choose to try that, you may do as you please; for I'm coming aboard of you as sure as heaven."

"Push off the bow there!" called the boatswain at the wheel. "Look alive! Why don't you push off the bow?"

"She's hard aground!" answerd the gunner. "We can't budge her an inch."

"If they was to fire into us now," said the sailing master, "they'd smash us to pieces."

"They won't fire into us," said the lieutenant. "They won't dare to." He jumped down from the cabin deckhouse as he spoke, and went forward to urge the men in pushing off the boat. It was already beginning to move.

At that moment the sailing master suddenly called out, "Mr. Maynard! Mr. Maynard! they're going to give us a broadside!"

Almost before the words were out of his mouth, before Lieutenant Maynard could turn, there came a loud and deafening crash, and then instantly another, and a third, and almost as instantly a crackling and rending of broken wood. There were clean yellow splinters flying everywhere. A man fell violently against the lieutenant, nearly overturning him, but he caught at the stays and so saved himself. For one tense moment he stood holding his breath. Then all about him arose a sudden outcry of groans and shouts and oats. The man who had fallen against him was lying face down upon the deck. His thighs were quivering, and a pool of blood was spreading and running out from under him. There were other men down, all about the deck. Some were rising; some were trying to rise; some only moved.

There was a distant sound of yelling and cheering and shouting. It was from the pirate sloop. The pirates were rushing about upon her decks. They had pulled the cannon back, and, through the grunting sound of the groans about him, the lieutenant could distinctly hear the thud and punch of the rammers, and he knew they were going to shoot again.

The low rail afforded almost no shelter against such a broadside, and there was nothing for it but to order all hands below for the time being.

"Get below!" roared out the lieutenant. "All hands get below and lie snug for further orders!" In obedience the men ran scrambling below into the hold, and in a little while the decks were nearly clear except for the three dead men and some three or four wounded. The boatswain, crouching down close to the wheel, and the lieutenant himself were the only others upon deck. Everywhere there were smears and sprinkles of blood. "Where's Brookes?" the lieutenant called out.

"He's hurt in the arm, sir, and he's gone below," said the boatswain.

Thereupon the lieutenant himself walked over to the forecastle hatch, and, hailing the gunner, ordered him to get up another ladder, so that the men could be run up on deck if the pirates should undertake to come aboard. At that moment the boatswain at the wheel called out that the villains were going to shoot again, and the lieutenant, turning, saw the gunner aboard of the pirate sloop in the act of touching the iron to the touchhole. He stooped down. There was another loud and deafening crash of cannon, one, two, three—four—the last two almost together—and almost instantly the boatswain called out, "'Tis the sloop, sir! look at the sloop!"

153

The sloop had got afloat again, and had been coming up to the aid of the schooner, when the pirates fired their second broadside now at her. When the lieutenant looked at her she was quivering with the impact of the shot, and the next moment she began falling off to the wind, and he could see the wounded men rising and falling and struggling upon her decks.

At the same moment the boatswain called out that the enemy was coming aboard, and even as he spoke the pirate sloop came drifting out from the cloud of smoke that enveloped her, looming up larger and larger as she came down upon them. The lieutenant still crouched down under the rail, looking out at them. Suddenly, a little distance away, she came about, broadside on, and then drifted. She was close aboard now. Something came flying through the air—another and another. They were bottles. One of them broke with a crash upon the deck. The others rolled over to the farther rail. In each of them a quick-match was smoking. Almost instantly there was a flash and a terrific report, and the air was full of the whiz and singing of broken particles of glass and iron. There was another report, and then the whole air seemed full of gunpowder smoke. "They're aboard of us!" shouted the boatswain, and even as he spoke the lieutenant roared out, "All hands to repel boarders!" A second later there came the heavy, thumping bump of the vessels coming together.

Lieutenant Maynard, as he called out the order, ran forward through the smoke, snatching one of his pistols out of his pocket and the cutlass out of its sheath as he did so. Behind him the men were coming, swarming up from below. There was a sudden stunning report of a pistol, and then another and another, almost together. There was a groan and the fall of a heavy body, and then a figure came jumping over the rail, with two or three more directly following. The lieutenant was

154

in the midst of the gunpowder smoke, when suddenly Black-beard was before him. The pirate captain had stripped him-self naked to the waist. His shaggy black hair was falling over his eyes, and he looked like a demon fresh from the pit, with his frantic face. Almost with the blindness of instinct the lieu-tenant thrust out his pistol, firing it as he did so. The pirate staggered back: he was down—no; he was up again. He had a pistol in each hand; but there was a stream of blood running down his naked ribs. Suddenly, the mouth of a pistol was pointing straight at the lieutenant's head. He ducked instinc-tively, striking upward with his cutlass as he did so. There was a stunning, deafening report almost in his ear. He struck again blindly with his cutlass. He saw the flash of a sword and flung up his guard almost instinctively, meeting the crash of the descending blade. Somebody shot from behind him, and at the same moment he saw some one else strike the pirate. Blackbeard staggered again, and this time there was a great gash upon his neck. Then one of Maynard's own men tumbled headlong upon him. He fell with the man, but almost instantly he had scrambled to his feet again, and as he did so he saw that the pirate sloop had drifted a little away from them, and that their grappling irons had evidently parted. His hand was smarting as though struck with the lash of a whip. He looked around him; the pirate captain was nowhere to be seen—yes, there he was, lying by the rail. He raised himself upon his elbow, and the lieutenant saw that he was trying to point a pistol at him, with an arm that wavered and swayed blindly, the pistol nearly falling from his fingers. Suddenly his other elbow gave way and he fell down upon his face. He tried to raise himself—he fell down again. There was a report and a cloud of smoke, and when it cleared away Blackbeard had stag-gered up again. He was a terrible figure—his head nodding down upon his breast. Somebody shot again, and then the swaying figure toppled and fell. It lay still for a moment—then rolled over—then lay still again.

There was a loud splash of men jumping overboard, and then, almost instantly, the cry of "Quarter! quarter!" The lieutenant ran to the edge of the vessel. It was as he had thought: the grappling irons of the pirate sloop had parted, and it had drifted away. The few pirates who had been left aboard of the schooner had jumped overboard and were now holding up their hands. "Quarter!" they cried. "Don't shoot!—quarter!" And the fight was over.

The lieutenant looked down at his hand, and then he saw, for the first time, that there was a great cutlass gash across the back of it, and that his arm and shirt sleeve were wet with blood. He went aft, holding the wrist of his wounded hand. The boatswain was still at the wheel. "By zounds!" said the lieutenant, with a nervous, quavering laugh, "I didn't know there was such fight in the villains."

His wounded and shattered sloop was again coming up toward him under sail, but the pirates had surrendered, and the fight was over.

VI

BLUESKIN, THE PIRATE

APE MAY and Cape Henlopen form, as it were, the upper and lower jaws of a gigantic mouth, which disgorges from its monstrous gullet the cloudy waters of the Delaware Bay into the heaving, sparkling blue-green of the Atlantic Ocean. From Cape Henlopen as the lower jaw there juts out a long, curving fang of high, smooth-rolling sand dunes, cutting sharp and clean against the still, blue sky above—silent, naked, utterly deserted, excepting for the squat, white-walled lighthouse standing upon the crest of the highest hill. Within this curving, sheltering hook of sand hills lie the smooth waters of Lewes Harbor, and, set a little back from the shore, the quaint old town, with its dingy wooden houses of clapboard and shingle, looks sleepily out through the masts of the shipping lying at anchor in the harbor, to the purple, clean-cut, level thread of the ocean horizon beyond.

Lewes is a queer, odd, old-fashioned little town, smelling fragrant of salt marsh and sea breeze. It is rarely visited by strangers. The people who live there are the progeny of people who have lived there for many generations, and it is the very place to nurse, and preserve, and care for old legends and traditions of bygone times, until they grow from bits of gossip and news into local history of considerable size. As in the busier world men talk of last year's elections, here these old bits, and scraps, and odds and ends of history are retailed to the listener who cares to listen—traditions of the War of 1812, when Beresford's fleet lay off the harbor threatening to bombard the town; tales of the Revolution and of Earl Howe's warships, tarrying for a while in the quiet harbor before they sailed up the river to shake old Philadelphia town with the thunders of their guns at Red Bank and Fort Mifflin.

With these substantial and sober threads of real history, other and more lurid colors are interwoven into the web of local lore—legends of the dark doings of famous pirates, of their mysterious, sinister comings and goings, of treasures buried in the sand dunes and pine barrens back of the cape and along the Atlantic beach to the southward.

Of such is the story of Blueskin, the pirate.

2

It was in the fall and the early winter of the year 1750, and again in the summer of the year following, that the famous pirate, Blueskin, became especially identified with Lewes as a part of its traditional history.

For some time—for three or four years—rumors and reports of Blueskin's doings in the West Indies and off the Carolinas had been brought in now and then by sea captains. There was no more cruel, bloody, desperate, devilish pirate than he in all those pirate-infested waters. All kinds of wild and bloody stories were current concerning him, but it never occurred to the good folk of Lewes that such stories were some time to be a part of their own history.

But one day a schooner came drifting into Lewes harbor— shattered, wounded, her forecastle splintered, her foremast shot half away, and three great tattered holes in her mainsail. The mate with one of the crew came ashore in the boat for help and a doctor. He reported that the captain and the cook were dead and there were three wounded men aboard. The story he told to the gathering crowd brought a very peculiar thrill to those who heard it. They had fallen in with Blueskin, he said, off Fenwick's Island (some twenty or thirty miles below the capes), and the pirates had come aboard of them; but, finding that the cargo of the schooner consisted only of cypress shingles and lumber, had soon quitted their prize. Perhaps Blueskin was disappointed at not finding a more valuable capture; perhaps the spirit of deviltry was hotter in him that morning than usual; anyhow, as the pirate craft bore away she fired three broadsides at short range into the helpless coaster. The captain had been killed at the first fire, the cook had died on the way up, three of the crew were wounded, and the vessel was leaking fast, betwixt wind and water.

Such was the mate's story. It spread like wildfire, and in half an hour all the town was in a ferment. Fenwick's Island was very near home; Blueskin might come sailing into the harbor at any minute and then—! In an hour Sheriff Jones had called together most of the able-bodied men of the town, muskets and rifles were taken down from the chimney places, and every preparation was made to defend the place against the pirates, should they come into the harbor and attempt to land.

But Blueskin did not come that day, nor did he come the next or the next. But on the afternoon of the third the news went suddenly flying over the town that the pirates were inside the capes. As the report spread the people came running— men, women, and children—to the green before the tavern, where a little knot of old seamen were gathered together, look- ing fixedly out toward the offing, talking in low voices. Two vessels, one bark-rigged, the other and smaller a sloop, were slowly creeping up the bay, a couple of miles or so away and just inside the cape. There appeared nothing remarkable about

159

the two crafts, but the little crowd that continued gathering upon the green stood looking out across the bay at them none the less anxiously for that. They were sailing close-hauled to the wind, the sloop following in the wake of her consort as the pilot fish follows in the wake of the shark.

But the course they held did not lie toward the harbor, but rather bore away toward the Jersey shore, and by and by it began to be apparent that Blueskin did not intend visiting the town. Nevertheless, those who stood looking did not draw a free breath until, after watching the two pirates for more than an hour and a half, they saw them—then about six mile away —suddenly put about and sail with a free wind out to sea again.

"The bloody villains have gone!" said old Captain Wolfe, shutting his telescope with a click.

But Lewes was not yet quit of Blueskin. Two days later a half-breed from Indian River bay came up, bringing the news that the pirates had sailed into the inlet—some fifteen miles below Lewes—and had careened the bark to clean her.

Perhaps Blueskin did not care to stir up the country people against him, for the half-breed reported that the pirates were doing no harm, and that what they took from the farmers of Indian River and Rehoboth they paid for with good hard money.

It was while the excitement over the pirates was at its highest fever heat that Levi West came home again.

3

Even in the middle of the last century the grist mill, a couple of miles from Lewes, although it was at most but fifty or sixty years old, had all a look of weather-beaten age, for the cypress shingles, of which it was built, ripen in a few years of wind and weather to a silvery, hoary gray, and the white powdering of flour lent it a look as though the dust of ages had settled upon it, making the shadows within dim, soft, mysterious. A dozen willow trees shaded with dappling, shivering ripples of shadow the road before the mill door, and the mill itself, and the long, narrow, shingle-built, one storied, hip-roofed dwelling house. At the time of the story the mill had descended in a direct line of succession to Hiram White, the grandson of old Ephraim White, who had built it, it was said, in 1701.

Hiram White was only twenty-seven years old, but he was already in local repute as a "character." As a boy he was thought to be half-witted or "natural," and, as is the case with such unfortunates in small country towns where everybody knows everybody, he was made a common sport and jest for the keener, crueler wits of the neighborhood. Now that he was grown to the ripeness of manhood he was still looked upon as being—to use a quaint expression—"slack," or "not jest right." He was heavy, awkward, ungainly and loose-jointed, and enormously, prodigiously strong. He had a lumpish, thick-featured face, with lips heavy and loosely hanging, that gave him an air of stupidity, half droll, half pathetic. His little eyes were set far apart and flat with his face, his eyebrows were nearly white and his hair was of a sandy, colorless kind. He was singularly taciturn, lisping thickly when he did talk, and stuttering and hesitating in his speech, as though his words moved faster than his mind could follow. It was the custom for local wags to urge, or badger, or tempt him to talk, for the sake of the ready laugh that always followed the few thick, stammering words and the stupid drooping of the jaw at the end of each short speech. Perhaps Squire Hall was the only one in Lewes Hundred who misdoubted that Hiram was half-witted. He had had dealings with him and was wont to say that whoever bought Hiram White for a fool made a fool's bargain. Certainly,

161

whether he had common wits or no, Hiram had managed his mill to pretty good purpose and was fairly well off in the world as prosperity went in southern Delaware and in those days. No doubt, had it come to the pinch, he might have bought some of his tormentors out three times over.

Hiram White had suffered quite a financial loss some six months before, through that very Blueskin who was now lurking in Indian River inlet. He had entered into a "venture" with Josiah Shippin, a Philadelphia merchant, to the tune of seven hundred pounds sterling. The money had been invested in a cargo of flour and corn meal which had been shipped to Jamaica by the bark *Nancy Lee*. The *Nancy Lee* had been captured by the pirates off Currituck Sound, the crew set adrift in the longboat, and the bark herself and all her cargo burned to the water's edge.

Five hundred of the seven hundred pounds invested in the unfortunate "venture" was money bequeathed by Hiram's father, seven years before, to Levi West.

Eleazer White had been twice married, the second time to the widow West. She had brought with her to her new home a good-looking, long-legged, black-eyed, black-haired ne'er-do-well of a son, a year or so younger than Hiram. He was a shrewd, quick-witted lad, idle, shiftless, willful, ill-trained perhaps, but as bright and keen as a pin. He was the very opposite to poor, dull Hiram. Eleazer White had never loved his son; he was ashamed of the poor, slack-witted oaf. Upon the other hand, he was very fond of Levi West, whom he always called "our Levi," and whom he treated in every way as though he were his own son. He tried to train the lad to work in the mill, and was patient beyond what the patience of most fathers would have been with his stepson's idleness and shiftlessness. "Never mind," he was used to say. "Levi'll come all right. Levi's as bright as a button."

162

It was one of the greatest blows of the old miller's life when Levi ran away to sea. In his last sickness the old man's mind constantly turned to his lost stepson. "Mebby he'll come back again," said he, "and if he does I want you to be good to him, Hiram. I've done my duty by you and have left you the house and mill, but I want you to promise that if Levi comes back again you'll give him a home and a shelter under this roof if he wants one." And Hiram had promised to do as his father asked.

After Eleazer died it was found that he had bequeathed five hundred pounds to his "beloved stepson, Levi West," and had left Squire Hall as trustee.

Levi West had been gone nearly nine years and not a word had been heard from him; there could be little or no doubt that he was dead.

One day Hiram came into Squire Hall's office with a letter in his hand. It was the time of the old French war, and flour and corn meal were fetching fabulous prices in the British West Indies. The letter Hiram brought with him was from a Philadelphia merchant, Josiah Shippin, with whom he had had some dealings. Mr. Shippin proposed that Hiram should join him in sending a "venture" of flour and corn meal to Kingston, Jamaica. Hiram had slept upon the letter overnight and now he brought it to the old Squire. Squire Hall read the letter, shaking his head the while. "To much risk, Hiram!" said he. "Mr. Shippin wouldn't have asked you to go into this venture if he could have got anybody else to do so. My advice is that you let it alone. I reckon you've come to me for advice?" Hiram shook his head. "Ye haven't? What have ye come for, then?"

"Seven hundred pounds," said Hiram.

"Seven hundred pounds!" said Squire Hall. "I haven't got seven hundred pounds to lend you, Hiram."

"Five hundred been left to Levi—I got hundred—raise hundred more on mortgage," said Hiram.

"Tut, tut, Hiram," said Squire Hall, "that 'll never do in the world. Suppose Levi West should come back again, what then? I'm responsible for that money. If you wanted to borrow it now for any reasonable venture, you should have it and welcome, but for such a wildcat scheme—"

"Levi never come back," said Hiram—"nine years gone—Levi's dead."

"Mebby he is," said Squire Hall, "but we don't know that."

"I'll give bond for security," said Hiram.

Squire Hall thought for a while in silence. "Very well, Hiram," said he by and by, "if you'll do that. Your father left the money, and I don't see that it's right for me to stay his son from using it. But if it is lost, Hiram, and if Levi should come back, it will go well to ruin ye."

So Hiram White invested seven hundred pounds in the Jamaica venture and every farthing of it was burned by Blueskin, off Currituck Sound.

4

Sally Martin was said to be the prettiest girl in Lewes Hundred, and when the rumor began to leak out that Hiram White was courting her the whole community took it as a monstrous joke. It was the common thing to greet Hiram himself with, "Hey, Hiram; how's Sally?" Hiram never made answer to such salutation, but went his way as heavily, as impassively, as dully as ever.

The joke was true. Twice a week, rain or shine, Hiram White never failed to scrape his feet upon Billy Martin's doorstep. Twice a week, on Sundays and Thursdays, he never failed to take his customary seat by the kitchen fire. He rarely said anything by way of talk; he nodded to the farmer, to his

Extorting Tribute from the Citizens

wife, to Sally and, when he chanced to be at home, to her brother, but he ventured nothing further. There he would sit from half past seven until nine o'clock, stolid, heavy, impassive, his dull eyes following now one of the family and now another, but always coming back again to Sally. It sometimes happened that she had other company—some of the young men of the neighborhood. The presence of such seemed to make no difference to Hiram; he bore whatever broad jokes might be cracked upon him, whatever grins, whatever giggling might follow those jokes, with the same patient impassiveness. There he would sit, silent, unresponsive; then at the first stroke of nine o'clock, he would rise, shoulder his ungainly person into his overcoat, twist his head into his three-cornered hat, and with a "Good night, Sally, I be going now," would take his departure, shutting the door carefully to behind him.

Never, perhaps, was there a girl in the world had such a lover and such a courtship as Sally Martin.

5

It was one Thursday evening in the latter part of November, about a week after Blueskin's appearance off the capes, and while the one subject of talk was of the pirates being in Indian River inlet. The air was still and wintry; a sudden cold snap had set in and skims of ice had formed over puddles in the road; the smoke from the chimneys rose straight in the quiet air and voices sounded loud, as they do in frosty weather.

Hiram White sat by the dim light of a tallow dip, poring laboriously over some account books. It was not quite seven o'clock, and he never started for Billy Martin's before that hour. As he ran his finger slowly and hesitatingly down the column of figures, he heard the kitchen door beyond open and shut, the noise of footsteps crossing the floor and the scraping of a chair dragged forward to the hearth. Then came the sound of a basket of corncobs being emptied on the smoldering blaze and then the snapping and crackling of the reanimated fire. Hiram thought nothing of all this, excepting, in a dim sort of way, that it was Bob, the negro mill hand, or old black Dinah, the housekeeper, and so went on with his calculations.

At last he closed the books with a snap and, smoothing down his hair, arose, took up the candle, and passed out of the room into the kitchen beyond.

A man was sitting in front of the corncob fire that flamed and blazed in the great, gaping, sooty fireplace. A rough over-coat was flung over the chair behind him and his hands were spread out to the roaring warmth. At the sound of the lifted latch and of Hiram's entrance he turned his head, and when Hiram saw his face he stood suddenly still as though turned to stone. The face, marvelously altered and changed as it was, was the face of his stepbrother, Levi West. He was not dead; he had come home again. For a time not a sound broke the dead, unbroken silence excepting the crackling of the blaze in the fireplace and the sharp ticking of the tall clock in the corner. The one face, dull and stolid, with the light of the candle shinging upward over its lumpy features, looked fixedly, immovably, stonily at the other, sharp, shrewd, cunning—the red wavering light of the blaze shining upon the high cheek bones, cutting sharp on the nose and twinkling in the glassy turn of the black, ratlike eyes. Then suddenly that face cracked, broadened, spread to a grin. "I have come back again, Hi," said Levi, and at the sound of the words the speechless spell was broken.

Hiram answered never a word, but he walked to the fire-place, set the candle down upon the dusty mantelshelf among the boxes and bottles, and, drawing forward a chair upon the other side of the hearth, sat down.

His dull little eyes never moved from his stepbrother's face.

166

There was no curiosity in his expression, no surprise, no wonder. The heavy under lip dropped a little farther open and there was more than usual of dull, expressionless stupidity upon the lumpish face; but that was all.

As was said, the face upon which he looked was strangely, marvelously changed from what it had been when he had last seen it nine years before, and, though it was still the face of Levi West, it was a very different Levi West than the shiftless ne'er-do-well who had run away to sea in the Brazilian brig that long time ago. That Levi West had been a rough, careless, happy-go-lucky fellow; thoughtless and selfish, but with nothing essentially evil or sinister in his nature. The Levi West that now sat in a rush-bottom chair at the other side of the fireplace had that stamped upon his front that might be both evil and sinister. His swart complexion was tanned to an Indian copper. On one side of his face was a curious discoloration in the skin and a long, crooked, cruel scar that ran diagonally across forehead and temple and cheek in a white, jagged seam. This discoloration was of a livid blue, about the tint of a tattoo mark. It made a patch the size of a man's hand, lying across the cheek and the side of the neck. Hiram could not keep his eyes from this mark and the white scar cutting across it.

There was an odd sort of incongruity in Levi's dress; a pair of heavy gold earrings and a dirty red handkerchief knotted loosely around his neck, beneath an open collar, displaying to its full length the lean, sinewy throat with its bony "Adam's apple," gave to his costume somewhat the smack of a sailor. He wore a coat that had once been of fine plum color—now stained and faded—too small for his lean length, and furbished with tarnished lace. Dirty cambric cuffs hung at his wrist and on his fingers were a half a dozen and more rings, set with stones that shone, and glistened, and twinkled in the light of the fire.

The hair at either temple was twisted into a Spanish curl, plastered flat to the cheek, and a plaited queue hung halfway down his back.

Hiram, speaking never a word, sat motionless, his dull little eyes traveling slowly up and down and around and around his stepbrother's person.

Levi did not seem to notice his scrutiny, leaning forward, now with his palms spread out to the grateful warmth, now rubbing them slowly together. But at last he suddenly whirled his chair around rasping on the floor, and faced his stepbrother. He thrust his hand into his capacious coat pocket and brought out a pipe which he proceeded to fill from a skin of tobacco. "Well, Hi," said he, "d'ye see I've come back home again?"

"Thought you was dead," said Hiram, dully.

Levi laughed, then he drew a red-hot coat out of the fire, put it upon the bowl of the pipe and began puffing out clouds of pungent smoke. "Nay, nay," said he; "not dead—not dead by odds. But [puff] by the Eternal Holy, Hi, I played many a close game [puff] with old Davy Jones, for all that."

Hiram's look turned inquiringly toward the jagged scar and Levi caught the slow glance. "You're lookin' at this," said he, running his finger down the crooked seam. "That looks bad, but it wasn't so close as this"—laying his hand for a moment upon the livid stain. "A cooly devil off Singapore gave me that cut when we fell foul of an opium junk in the China Sea four years ago last September. This," touching the disfiguring blue patch again, "was a closer miss, Hi. A Spanish captain fired a pistol at me down off Santa Catharina. He was so nigh that the powder went under the skin and it 'll never come out out again. ——his eyes—he had better have fired the pistol into his own head that morning. But never mind that. I reckon I'm changed, ain't I, Hi?"

168

He took his pipe out of his mouth and looked inquiringly at Hiram, who nodded.

Levi laughed. "Devil doubt it," said he, "but whether I'm changed or no, I'll take my affidavy that you are the same old half-witted Hi that you used to be. I remember dad used to say that you hadn't no more than enough wits to keep you out of the rain. And, talking of dad, Hi, I hearn tell he's been dead now these nine years gone. D'ye know what I've come home for?"

Hiram shook his head.

"I've come for that five hundred pounds that dad left me when he died, for I hearn tell of that, too."

Hiram sat quite still for a second or two and then he said, "I put that money out to venture and lost it all."

Levi's face fell and he took his pipe out of his mouth, regarding Hiram sharply and keenly. "What d'ye mean?" said he presently.

"I thought you was dead—and I put—seven hundred pounds—into *Nancy Lee*—and Blueskin burned her—off Currituck."

"Burned her off Currituck!" repeated Levi. Then suddenly a light seemed to break upon his comprehension. "Burned by Blueskin!" he repeated, and thereupon flung himself back in his chair and burst into a short, boisterous fit of laughter. "Well, by the Holy Eternal, Hi, if that isn't a piece of your tarnal luck. Burned by Blueskin, was it?" He paused for a moment, as though turning it over in his mind. Then he laughed again. "All the same," said he presently, "d'ye see, I can't suffer for Blueskin's doings. The money was willed to me, fair and true, and you have got to pay it, Hiram White, burn or sink, Blueskin or no Blueskin." Again he puffed for a moment or two in reflective silence. "All the same, Hi," said

169

he, once more resuming the thread of talk, "I don't reckon to be too hard on you. You be only half-witted, anyway, and I sha'n't be too hard on you. I give you a month to raise that money, and while you're doing it I'll jest hang around here. I've been in trouble, Hi, d'ye see. I'm under a cloud and so I want to keep here, as quiet as may be. I'll tell ye how it came about: I had a set-to with a land pirate in Philadelphia, and somebody got hurt. That's the reason I'm here now, and don't you say anything about it. Do you understand?"

Hiram opened his lips as though it was his intent to answer, then seemed to think better of it and contented himself by nodding his head.

That Thursday night was the first for a six-month that Hiram White did not scrape his feet clean at Billy Martin's doorstep.

6

Within a week Levi West had pretty well established himself among his old friends and acquaintances, though upon a different footing from that of nine years before, for this was a very different Levi from that other. Nevertheless, he was none the less popular in the barroom of the tavern and at the country store, where he was always the center of a group of loungers. His nine years seemed to have been crowded full of the wildest of wild adventures and happenings, as well by land as by sea, and, given an appreciative audience, he would reel off his yarns by the hour, in a reckless, devil-may-care fashion that set agape even old sea dogs who had sailed the western ocean since boyhood. Then he seemed always to have plenty of money, and he loved to spend it at the tavern taproom, with a lavishness that was at once the wonder and admiration of gossips.

170

At that time, as was said, Blueskin was the one engrossing topic of talk, and it added not a little to Levi's prestige when it was found that he had actually often seen that bloody, devilish pirate with his own eyes. A great, heavy, burly fellow, Levi said he was, with a beard as black as a hat—a devil with his sword and pistol afloat, but not so black as he was painted when ashore. He told of many adventures in which Blueskin figured and was then always listened to with more than usual gaping interest.

As for Blueskin, the quiet way in which the pirates conducted themselves at Indian River almost made the Lewes folk forget what he could do when the occasion called. They almost ceased to remember that poor shattered schooner that had crawled with its ghastly dead and groaning wounded into the harbor a couple of weeks since. But if for a while they forgot who or what Blueskin was, it was not for long.

One day a bark from Bristol, bound for Cuba and laden with a valuable cargo of cloth stuffs and silks, put into Lewes harbor to take in water. The captain himself came ashore and was at the tavern for two or three hours. It happened that Levi was there and that the talk was of Blueskin. The English captain, a grizzled old sea dog, listened to Levi's yarns with not a little contempt. He had, he said, sailed in the China Sea and the Indian Ocean too long to be afraid of any hog-eating Yankee pirate such as this Blueskin. A junk full of coolies armed with stink-pots was something to speak of, but who ever heard of the likes of Blueskin falling afoul of anything more than a Spanish canoe or a Yankee coaster?

Levi grinned. "All the same, my hearty," said he, "if I was you I'd give Blueskin a wide berth. I hear that he's cleaned the vessel that was careened awhile ago, and mebby he'll give you a little trouble if you come too nigh him."

To this the Englishman only answered that Blueskin might be———, and that the next afternoon, wind and weather permitting, he intended to heave anchor and run out to sea.

Levi laughed again. "I wish I might be here to see what'll happen," said he, "but I'm going up the river to-night to see a gal and mebby won't be back again for three or four days."

The next afternoon the English bark set sail as the captain promised, and that night Lewes town was awake until almost morning, gazing at a broad red glare that lighted up the sky away toward the southeast. Two days afterward a negro oysterman came up from Indian River with news that the pirates were lying off the inlet, bringing ashore bales of goods from their larger vessel and piling the same upon the beach under tarpaulins. He said that it was known down at Indian River that Blueskin had fallen afoul of an English bark, had burned her and had murdered the captain and all but three of the crew, who had joined with the pirates.

The excitement over this terrible happening had only begun to subside when another occurred to cap it. One afternoon a ship's boat, in which were five men and two women, came rowing into Lewes harbor. It was the longboat of the Charleston packet, bound for New York, and was commanded by the first mate. The packet had been attacked and captured by the pirates about ten leagues south by east of Cape Henlopen. The pirates had come aboard of them at night and no resistance had been offered. Perhaps it was that circumstance that saved the lives of all, for no murder or violence had been done. Nevertheless, officers, passengers and crew had been stripped of everything of value and set adrift in the boats and the ship herself had been burned. The longboat had become separated from the others during the night and had sighted Henlopen a little after sunrise.

It may be here said that Squire Hall made out a report of
these two occurrences and sent it up to Philadelphia by the
mate of the packet. But for some reason it was nearly four
weeks before a sloop of war was sent around from New York.
In the meanwhile, the pirates had disposed of the booty stored
under the tarpaulins on the beach at Indian River inlet, shipping some of it away in two small sloops and sending the rest
by wagons somewhere up the country.

7

Levi had told the English captain that he was going up-
country to visit one of his lady friends. He was gone nearly
two weeks. Then once more he appeared, as suddenly, as unexpectedly, as he had done when he first returned to Lewes.
Hiram was sitting at supper when the door opened and Levi
walked in, hanging up his hat behind the door as unconcern-
edly as though he had only been gone an hour. He was in an
ugly, lowering humor and sat himself down at the table without uttering a word, resting his chin upon his clenched fist and
glowering fixedly at the corn cake while Dinah fetched him a
plate and knife and fork.

His coming seemed to have taken away all of Hiram's appetite. He pushed away his plate and sat staring at his stepbrother, who presently fell to at the bacon and eggs like a
famished wolf. Not a word was said until Levi had ended his
meal and filled his pipe. "Look'ee, Hiram," said he, as he
stooped over the fire and raked out a hot coal. "Look'ee,
Hiram! I've been to Philadelphia, d'ye see, a-settlin' up that
trouble I told you about when I first come home. D'ye understand? D'ye remember? D'ye get it through your skull?" He
looked around over his shoulder, waiting as though for an
answer. But getting none, he continued: "I expect two gentle-

173

men here from Philadelphia to-night. They're friends of mine and are coming to talk over the business and ye needn't stay at home, Hi. You can go out somewhere, d'ye understand?" And then he added with a grin, "Ye can go to see Sally."

Hiram pushed back his chair and arose. He leaned with his back against the side of the fireplace. "I'll stay at home," said he presently.

"But I don't want you to stay at home, Hi," said Levi. "We'll have to talk business and I want you to go!"

"I'll stay at home," said Hiram again.

Levi's brow grew as black as thunder. He ground his teeth together and for a moment or two it seemed as though an explosion was coming. But he swallowed his passion with a gulp. "You're a —— pig-headed, half-witted fool," said he. Hiram never so much as moved his eyes. "As for you," said Levi, whirling round upon Dinah, who was clearing the table, and glowering balefully upon the old negress, "you put them things down and git out of here. Don't you come nigh this kitchen again till I tell ye to. If I catch you pryin' around may I be ——, eyes and liver, if I don't cut your heart out."

In about half an hour Levi's friends came; the first a little thin, wizened man with a very foreign look. He was dressed in a rusty black suit and wore gray yarn stockings and shoes with brass buckles. The other was also plainly a foreigner. He was dressed in sailor fashion, with petticoat breeches of duck, a heavy pea-jacket, and thick boots, reaching to the knees. He wore a red sash tied around his waist, and once, as he pushed back his coat, Hiram saw the glitter of a pistol butt. He was a powerful, thickset man, low-browed and bull-necked, his cheek, and chin, and throat closely covered with a stubble of blue-black beard. He wore a red kerchief tied around his head and over it a cocked hat, edged with tarnished gilt braid.

174

Levi himself opened the door to them. He exchanged a few words outside with his visitors, in a foreign language of which Hiram understood nothing. Neither of the two strangers spoke a word to Hiram: the little man shot him a sharp look out of the corners of his eyes and the burly ruffian scowled blackly at him, but beyond that neither vouchsafed him any regard.

Levi drew to the shutters, shot the bolt in the outer door, and tilted a chair against the latch of the one that led from the kitchen into the adjoining room. Then the three worthies seated themselves at the table which Dinah had half cleared of the supper china, and were presently deeply engrossed over a packet of papers which the big, burly man had brought with him in the pocket of his pea-jacket. The confabulation was conducted throughout in the same foreign language which Levi had used when first speaking to them—a language quite unintelligible to Hiram's ears. Now and then the murmur of talk would rise loud and harsh over some disputed point; now and then it would sink away to whispers.

Twice the tall clock in the corner whirred and sharply struck the hour, but throughout the whole long consultation Hiram stood silent, motionless as a stock, his eyes fixed almost unwinkingly upon the three heads grouped close together around the dim, flickering light of the candle and the papers scattered upon the table.

Suddenly the talk came to an end, the three heads separated and the three chairs were pushed back, grating harshly. Levi rose, went to the closet and brought thence a bottle of Hiram's apple brandy, as coolly as though it belonged to himself. He set three tumblers and a crock of water upon the table and each helped himself liberally.

As the two visitors departed down the road, Levi stood for a while at the open door, looking after the dusky figures until they were swallowed in the darkness. Then he turned, came in, shut the door, shuddered, took a final dose of the apple brandy and went to bed, without, since his first suppressed explosion, having said a single word to Hiram.

Hiram, left alone, stood for a while, silent, motionless as ever, then he looked slowly about him, gave a shake of the shoulders as though to arouse himself, and taking the candle, left the room, shutting the door noiselessly behind him.

8

This time of Levi West's unwelcome visitation was indeed a time of bitter trouble and tribulation to poor Hiram White. Money was of very different value in those days than it is now, and five hundred pounds was in its way a good round lump—in Sussex County it was almost a fortune. It was a desperate struggle for Hiram to raise the amount of his father's bequest to his stepbrother. Squire Hall, as may have been gathered, had a very warm and friendly feeling for Hiram, believing in him when all others disbelieved; nevertheless, in the matter of money the old man was as hard and as cold as adamant. He would, he said, do all he could to help Hiram, but that five hundred pounds must and should be raised—Hiram must release his security bond. He would loan him, he said, three hundred pounds, taking a mortgage upon the mill. He would have lent him four hundred but that there was already a first-mortgage of one hundred pounds upon it, and he would not dare to put more than three hundred more atop of that.

Hiram had a considerable quantity of wheat which he had bought upon speculation and which was then lying idle in a Philadelphia storehouse. This he had sold at public sale and at a very great sacrifice; he realized barely one hundred pounds upon it. The financial horizon looked very black to him;

nevertheless, Levi's five hundred pounds was raised, and paid into Squire Hall's hands, and Squire Hall released Hiram's bond.

The business was finally closed on one cold, gray afternoon in the early part of December. As Hiram tore his bond across and then tore it across again and again, Squire Hall pushed back the papers upon his desk and cocked his feet upon its slanting top. "Hiram," said he, abruptly, "Hiram, do you know that Levi West is forever hanging around Billy Martin's house, after that pretty daughter of his?"

So long a space of silence followed the speech that the Squire began to think that Hiram might not have heard him. But Hiram had heard. "No," said he, "I didn't know it."

"Well, he is," said Squire Hall. "It's the talk of the whole neighborhood. The talk's pretty bad, too. D'ye know that they say that she was away from home three days last week, nobody knew where? The fellow's turned her head with his sailor's yarns and his traveler's lies."

Hiram said not a word, but he sat looking at the other in stolid silence. "That stepbrother of yours," continued the old Squire presently, "is a rascal—he is a rascal, Hiram, and I misdoubt he's something worse. I hear he's been seen in some queer places and with queer company of late."

He stopped again, and still Hiram said nothing. "And look'ee, Hiram," the old man resumed, suddenly, "I do hear that you be courtin' the girl, too; is that so?"

"Yes," said Hiram, "I'm courtin' her, too."

"Tut! tut!" said the Squire, "that's a pity, Hiram. I'm afraid your cakes are dough."

After he had left the Squire's office, Hiram stood for a while in the street, bareheaded, his hat in his hand, staring unwinkingly down at the ground at his feet, with stupidly drooping

177

lips and lackluster eyes. Presently he raised his hand and began slowly smoothing down the sandy shock of hair upon his forehead. At last he aroused himself with a shake, looked dully up and down the street, and then, putting on his hat, turned and walked slowly and heavily away.

The early dusk of the cloudy winter evening was settling fast, for the sky was leaden and threatening. At the outskirts of the town Hiram stopped again and again stood for a while in brooding thought. Then, finally, he turned slowly, not the way that led homeward, but taking the road that led between the bare and withered fields and crooked fences toward Billy Martin's.

It would be hard to say just what it was that led Hiram to seek Billy Martin's house at that time of day—whether it was fate or ill fortune. He could not have chosen a more opportune time to confirm his own undoing. What he saw was the very worst that his heart feared.

Along the road, at a little distance from the house, was a mock-orange hedge, now bare, naked, leafless. As Hiram drew near he heard footsteps approaching and low voices. He drew back into the fence corner and there stood, half sheltered by the stark network of twigs. Two figures passed slowly along the gray of the roadway in the gloaming. One was his stepbrother, the other was Sally Martin. Levi's arm was around her, he was whispering into her ear, and her head rested upon his shoulder.

Hiram stood as still, as breathless, as cold as ice. They stopped upon the side of the road just beyond where he stood. Hiram's eyes never left them. There for some time they talked together in low voices, their words now and then reaching the ears of that silent, breathless listener.

Suddenly there came the clattering of an opening door, and

then Betty Martin's voice broke the silence, harshly, shrilly: "Sal!—Sal!—Sally Martin! You, Sally Martin! Come in yere. Where be ye?"

The girl flung her arms around Levi's neck and their lips met in one quick kiss. The next moment she was gone, flying swiftly, silently, down the road past where Hiram stood, stooping as she ran. Levi stood looking after her until she was gone; then he turned and walked away whistling.

His whistling died shrilly into silence in the wintry distance, and then at last Hiram came stumbling out from the hedge. His face had never looked before as it looked then.

9

Hiram was standing in front of the fire with his hands clasped behind his back. He had not touched the supper on the table. Levi was eating with an appetite. Suddenly he looked over his plate at his stepbrother.

"How about that five hundred pounds, Hiram?" said he. "I gave ye a month to raise it and the month ain't quite up yet, but I'm goin' to leave this here place day after to-morrow —by next day at the furd'st—and I want the money that's mine."

"I paid it to Squire Hall to-day and he has it fer ye," said Hiram, dully.

Levi laid down his knife and fork with a clatter. "Squire Hall!" said he, "what's Squire Hall got to do with it? Squire Hall didn't have the use of that money. It was you had it and you have got to pay it back to me, and if you don't do it, by G——, I'll have the law on you, sure as you're born."

"Squire Hall's trustee—I ain't your trustee," said Hiram, in the same dull voice.

179

"I don't know nothing about trustees," said Levi, "or any-thing about lawyer business, either. What I want to know is, are you going to pay me my money or no?"

"No," said Hiram, "I ain't—Squire Hall'll pay ye; you go to him."

Levi West's face grew purple red. He pushed back, his chair grating harshly. "You—bloody land pirate!" he said, grinding his teeth together. "I see through your tricks. You're up to cheating me out of my money. You know very well that Squire Hall is down on me, hard and bitter—writin' his—— reports to Philadelphia and doing all he can to stir up every-body agin me and to bring the bluejackets down on me. I see through your tricks as clear as glass, but ye sha'n't trick me. I'll have my money if there's law in the land—ye bloody, un-natural thief ye, who'd go agin your dead father's will!"

Then—if the roof had fallen in upon him, Levi West could not have been more amazed—Hiram suddenly strode for-ward, and, leaning half across the table with his fists clenched, fairly glared into Levi's eyes. His face, dull, stupid, wooden, was now fairly convulsed with passion. The great veins stood out upon his temples like knotted whipcords, and when he spoke his voice was more a breathless snarl than the voice of a Christian man.

"Ye'll have the law, will ye?" said he. "Ye'll—have the law, will ye? You're afeared to go to law—Levi West—you try th' law—and see how ye like it. Who 're you to call me thief—ye bloody, murderin' villain ye! You're the thief—Levi West— you come here and stole my daddy from me—ye did. You make me ruin—myself to pay what oughter to been mine— then—ye—ye steal the gal I was courtin', to boot." He stopped and his lips writhed for words to say. "I know ye," said he, grinding his teeth. "I know ye! And only for what my

180

daddy made me promise I'd a-had you up to the magistrate's before this."

Then, pointing with quivering finger: "There's the door —you see it! Go out that there door and don't never come into it again—if ye do—or if ye ever come where I can lay eyes on ye again—by th' Holy Holy I'll hale ye up to the Squire's office and tell all I know and all I've seen. Oh, I'll give ye your belly-fill of law if—ye want th' law! Git out of the house, I say!"

As Hiram spoke Levi seemed to shrink together. His face changed from its copper color to a dull, waxy yellow. When the other ended he answered never a word. But he pushed back his chair, rose, put on his hat and, with a furtive, sidelong look, left the house, without stopping to finish the supper which he had begun. He never entered Hiram White's door again.

10

Hiram had driven out the evil spirit from his home, but the mischief that it had brewed was done and could not be undone. The next day it was known that Sally Martin had run away from home, and that she had run away with Levi West. Old Billy Martin had been in town in the morning with his rifle, hunting for Levi and threatening if he caught him to have his life for leading his daughter astray.

And, as the evil spirit had left Hiram's house, so had another and a greater evil spirit quitted its harborage. It was heard from Indian River in a few days more that Blueskin had quitted the inlet and had sailed away to the southeast; and it was reported, by those who seemed to know, that he had finally quitted those parts.

It was well for himself that Blueskin left when he did, for

181

not three days after he sailed away the *Scorpion* sloop-of-war dropped anchor in Lewes harbor. The New York agent of the unfortunate packet and a government commissioner had also come aboard the *Scorpion*.

Without loss of time, the officer in command instituted a keen and searching examination that brought to light some singularly curious facts. It was found that a very friendly understanding must have existed for some time between the pirates and the people of Indian River, for, in the houses throughout that section, many things—some of considerable value—that had been taken by the pirates from the packet, were discovered and seized by the commissioner. Valuables of a suspicious nature had found their way even into the houses of Lewes itself.

The whole neighborhood seemed to have become more or less tainted by the presence of the pirates.

Even poor Hiram White did not escape the suspicions of having had dealings with them. Of course the examiners were not slow in discovering that Levi West had been deeply concerned with Blueskin's doings.

Old Dinah and black Bob were examined, and not only did the story of Levi's two visitors come to light, but also the fact that Hiram was present and with them while they were in the house disposing of the captured goods to their agent.

Of all that he had endured, nothing seemed to cut poor Hiram so deeply and keenly as these unjust suspicions. They seemed to bring the last bitter pang, hardest of all to bear.

Levi had taken from him his father's love; he had driven him, if not to ruin, at least perilously close to it. He had run away with the girl he loved, and now, through him, even Hiram's good name was gone.

Neither did the suspicions against him remain passive; they became active.

Goldsmiths' bills, to the amount of several thousand pounds, had been taken in the packet and Hiram was examined with an almost inquisitorial closeness and strictness as to whether he had or had not knowledge of their whereabouts.

Under his accumulated misfortunes, he grew not only more dull, more taciturn, than ever, but gloomy, moody, brooding as well. For hours he would sit staring straight before him into the fire, without moving so much as a hair.

One night—it was a bitterly cold night in February, with three inches of dry and gritty snow upon the ground—while Hiram sat thus brooding, there came, of a sudden, a soft tap upon the door.

Low and hesitating as it was, Hiram started violently at the sound. He sat for a while, looking from right to left. Then suddenly pushing back his chair, he arose, strode to the door, and flung it wide open.

It was Sally Martin.

Hiram stood for a while staring blankly at her. It was she who first spoke. "Won't you let me come in, Hi?" said she. "I'm nigh starved with the cold and I'm fit to die, I'm so hungry. For God's sake, let me come in."

"Yes," said Hiram, "I'll let you come in, but why don't you go home?"

The poor girl was shivering and chattering with the cold; now she began crying, wiping her eyes with the corner of a blanket in which her head and shoulders were wrapped. "I have been home, Hiram," she said, "but dad, he shut the door in my face. He cursed me just awful, Hi—I wish I was dead!"

"You better come in," said Hiram. "It's no good standing out there in the cold." He stood aside and the girl entered, swiftly, gratefully.

At Hiram's bidding black Dinah presently set some food before Sally and she fell to eating ravenously, almost fero-

183

ciously. Meantime, while she ate, Hiram stood with his back to the fire, looking at her face—that face once so round and rosy, now thin, pinched, haggard.

"Are you sick, Sally?" said he presently.

"No," said she, "but I've had pretty hard times since I left home, Hi." The tears sprang to her eyes at the recollection of her troubles, but she only wiped them hastily away with the back of her hand, without stopping in her eating.

A long pause of dead silence followed. Dinah sat crouched together on a cricket at the other side of the hearth, listening with interest. Hiram did not seem to see her. "Did you go off with Levi?" said he at last, speaking abruptly. The girl looked up furtively under her brows. "You needn't be afeared to tell," he added.

"Yes," said she at last, "I did go off with him, Hi."

"Where've you been?"

At the question, she suddenly laid down her knife and fork. "Don't you ask me that, Hi," said she, agitatedly, "I can't tell you that. You don't know Levi, Hiram; I darsn't tell you anything he don't want me to. If I told you where I been he'd hunt me out, no matter where I was, and kill me. If you only knew what I know about him, Hiram, you wouldn't ask anything about him."

Hiram stood looking broodingly at her for a long time; then at last he again spoke. "I thought a sight of you onc't, Sally," said he.

Sally did not answer immediately, but, after a while, she suddenly looked up. "Hiram," said she, "if I tell ye something will you promise on your oath not to breathe a word to any living soul?" Hiram nodded. "Then I'll tell you, but if Levi finds I've told he'll murder me as sure as you're standin' there. Come nigher—I've got to whisper it." He leaned forward close

184

to her where she sat. She looked swiftly from right to left; then raising her lips she breathed into his ear: "I'm an honest woman, Hi. I was married to Levi West before I run away."

11

The winter had passed, spring had passed, and summer had come. Whatever Hiram had felt, he had made no sign of suffering. Nevertheless, his lumpy face had begun to look flabby, his cheeks hollow, and his loose-jointed body shrunk more awkwardly together into its clothes. He was often awake at night, sometimes walking up and down his room until far into the small hours.

It was through such a wakeful spell as this that he entered into the greatest, the most terrible, happening of his life.

It was a sulphurously hot night in July. The air was like the breath of a furnace, and it was a hard matter to sleep with even the easiest mind and under the most favorable circumstances. The full moon shone in through the open window, laying a white square of light upon the floor, and Hiram, as he paced up and down, up and down, walked directly through it, his gaunt figure starting out at every turn into sudden brightness as he entered the straight line of misty light.

The clock in the kitchen whirred and rang out the hour of twelve, and Hiram stopped in his walk to count the strokes.

The last vibration died away into silence, and still he stood motionless, now listening with a new and sudden intentness, for, even as the clock rang the last stroke, he heard soft, heavy footsteps, moving slowly and cautiously along the pathway before the house and directly below the open window. A few seconds more and he heard the creaking of rusty hinges. The mysterious visitor had entered the mill. Hiram crept softly to

185

the window and looked out. The moon shone full on the dusty, shingled face of the old mill, not thirty steps away, and he saw that the door was standing wide open. A second or two of stillness followed, and then, as he still stood looking intently, he saw the figure of a man suddenly appear, sharp and vivid, from the gaping blackness of the open doorway. Hiram could see his face as clear as day. It was Levi West, and he carried an empty meal bag over his arm.

Levi West stood looking from right to left for a second or two, and then he took off his hat and wiped his brow with the back of his hand. Then he softly closed the door behind him and left the mill as he had come, and with the same cautious step. Hiram looked down upon him as he passed close to the house and almost directly beneath. He could have touched him with his hand.

Fifty or sixty yards from the house Levi stopped and a second figure arose from the black shadow in the angle of the worm fence and joined him. They stood for a while talking together, Levi pointing now and then toward the mill. Then the two turned, and, climbing over the fence, cut across an open field and through the tall, shaggy grass toward the southeast.

Hiram straightened himself and drew a deep breath, and the moon, shining full upon his face, showed it twisted, convulsed, as it had been when he had fronted his stepbrother seven months before in the kitchen. Great beads of sweat stood on his brow and he wiped them away with his sleeve. Then, coatless, hatless as he was, he swung himself out of the window, dropped upon the grass, and, without an instant of hesitation, strode off down the road in the direction that Levi West had taken.

As he climbed the fence where the two men had climbed it

186

he could see them in the pallid light, far away across the level, scrubby meadow land, walking toward a narrow strip of pine woods.

A little later they entered the sharp-cut shadows beneath the trees and were swallowed in the darkness.

With fixed eyes and close-shut lips, as doggedly, as inexorably as though he were a Nemesis hunting his enemy down, Hiram followed their footsteps across the stretch of moonlit open. Then, by and by, he also was in the shadow of the pines. Here, not a sound broke the midnight hush. His feet made no noise upon the resinous softness of the ground below. In that dead, pulseless silence he could distinctly hear the distant voices of Levi and his companion, sounding loud and resonant in the hollow of the woods. Beyond the woods was a cornfield, and presently he heard the rattling of the harsh leaves as the two plunged into the tasseled jungle. Here, as in the woods, he followed them, step by step, guided by the noise of their progress through the canes.

Beyond the cornfield ran a road that, skirting to the south of Lewes, led across a wooden bridge to the wide salt marshes that stretched between the town and the distant sand hills. Coming out upon this road Hiram found that he had gained upon those he followed, and that they now were not fifty paces away, and he could see that Levi's companion carried over his shoulder what looked like a bundle of tools.

He waited for a little while to let them gain their distance and for the second time wiped his forehead with his shirt sleeve; then, without ever once letting his eyes leave them, he climbed the fence to the roadway.

For a couple of miles or more he followed the two along the white, level highway, past silent, sleeping houses, past barns, sheds, and haystacks, looming big in the moonlight, past fields,

187

and woods, and clearings, past the dark and silent skirts of the town, and so, at last, out upon the wide, misty salt marshes, which seemed to stretch away interminably through the pallid light, yet were bounded in the far distance by the long, white line of sand hills.

Across the level salt marshes he followed them, through the rank sedge and past the glassy pools in which his own inverted image stalked beneath as he stalked above; on and on, until at last they had reached a belt of scrub pines, gnarled and gray, that fringed the foot of the white sand hills.

Here Hiram kept within the black network of shadow. The two whom he followed walked more in the open, with their shadows, as black as ink, walking along in the sand beside them, and now, in the dead, breathless stillness, might be heard, dull and heavy, the distant thumping, pounding roar of the Atlantic surf, beating on the beach at the other side of the sand hills, half a mile away.

At last the two rounded the southern end of the white bluff, and when Hiram, following, rounded it also, they were no longer to be seen.

Before him the sand hill rose, smooth and steep, cutting in a sharp ridge against the sky. Up this steep hill trailed the footsteps of those he followed, disappearing over the crest. Beyond the ridge lay a round, bowl-like hollow, perhaps fifty feet across and eighteen or twenty feet deep, scooped out by the eddying of the winds into an almost perfect circle. Hiram, slowly, cautiously, stealthily, following their trailing line of footmarks, mounted to the top of the hillock and peered down into the bowl beneath. The two men were sitting upon the sand, not far from the tall, skeleton-like shaft of a dead pine tree that rose, stark and gray, from the sand in which it may once have been buried, centuries ago.

12

Levi had taken off his coat and waistcoat and was fanning himself with his hat. He was sitting upon the bag he had brought from the mill and which he had spread out upon the sand. His companion sat facing him. The moon shone full upon him and Hiram knew him instantly—he was the same burly, foreign-looking ruffian who had come with the little man to the mill that night to see Levi. He also had his hat off and was wiping his forehead and face with a red handkerchief. Beside him lay the bundle of tools he had brought—a couple of shovels, a piece of rope, and a long, sharp iron rod.

The two men were talking together, but Hiram could not understand what they said, for they spoke in the same foreign language that they had before used. But he could see his step-brother point with his finger, now to the dead tree and now to the steep, white face of the opposite side of the bowl-like hollow.

At last, having apparently rested themselves, the conference, if conference it was, came to an end, and Levi led the way, the other following, to the dead pine tree. Here he stopped and began searching, as though for some mark; then, having found that which he looked for, he drew a tapeline and a large brass pocket compass from his pocket. He gave one end of the tape line to his companion, holding the other with his thumb pressed upon a particular part of the tree. Taking his bearings by the compass, he gave now and then some orders to the other, who moved a little to the left or the right as he bade. At last he gave a word of command, and, thereupon, his companion drew a wooden peg from his pocket and thrust it into the sand. From this peg as a base they again measured, taking bearings by the compass, and again drove a peg. For a third time they repeated their measurements and

189

then, at last, seemed to have reached the point which they aimed for.

Here Levi marked a cross with his heel upon the sand.

His companion brought him the pointed iron rod which lay beside the shovels, and then stood watching as Levi thrust it deep into the sand, again and again, as though sounding for some object below. It was some while before he found that for which he was seeking, but at last the rod struck with a jar upon some hard object below. After making sure of success by one or two additional taps with the rod, Levi left it remaining where it stood, brushing the sand from his hands. "Now fetch the shovels, Pedro," said he, speaking for the first time in English.

The two men were busy for a long while, shoveling away the sand. The object for which they were seeking lay buried some six feet deep, and the work was heavy and laborious, the shifting sand sliding back, again and again, into the hole. But at last the blade of one of the shovels struck upon some hard substance and Levi stooped and brushed away the sand with the palm of his hand.

Levi's companion climbed out of the hole which they had dug and tossed the rope which he had brought with the shovels down to the other. Levi made it fast to some object below and then himself mounted to the level of the sand above. Pulling together, the two drew up from the hole a heavy iron-bound box, nearly three feet long and a foot wide and deep.

Levi's companion stooped and began untying the rope which had been lashed to a ring in the lid.

What next happened happened suddenly, swiftly, terribly. Levi drew back a single step, and shot one quick, keen look to right and to left. He passed his hand rapidly behind his back, and the next moment Hiram saw the moonlight gleam upon the long, sharp, keen blade of a knife. Levi raised his arm.

Then, just as the other arose from bending over the chest, he struck, and struck again, two swift, powerful blows. Hiram saw the blade drive, clean and sharp, into the back, and heard the hilt strike with a dull thud against the ribs—once, twice. The burly, black-bearded wretch gave a shrill, terrible cry and fell staggering back. Then, in an instant, with another cry, he was up and clutched Levi with a clutch of despair by the throat and by the arm. Then followed a struggle, short, terrible, silent. Not a sound was heard but the deep, panting breath and the scuffling of feet in the sand, upon which there now poured and dabbled a dark-purple stream. But it was a one-sided struggle and lasted only for a second or two. Levi wrenched his arm loose from the wounded man's grasp, tearing his shirt sleeve from the wrist to the shoulder as he did so. Again and again the cruel knife was lifted, and again and again it fell, now no longer bright, but stained with red.

Then, suddenly, all was over. Levi's companion dropped to the sand without a sound, like a bundle of rags. For a moment he lay limp and inert; then one shuddering spasm passed over him and he lay silent and still, with his face half buried in the sand.

Levi, with the knife still gripped tight in his hand, stood leaning over his victim, looking down upon his body. His shirt and hand, and even his naked arm, were stained and blotched with blood. The moon lit up his face and it was the face of a devil from hell.

At last he gave himself a shake, stooped and wiped his knife and hand and arm upon the loose petticoat breeches of the dead man. He thrust his knife back into its sheath, drew a key from his pocket and unlocked the chest. In the moonlight Hiram could see that it was filled mostly with paper and leather bags, full, apparently of money.

All through this awful struggle and its awful ending Hiram

191

lay, dumb and motionless, upon the crest of the sand hill, looking with a horrid fascination upon the death struggle in the pit
below. Now Hiram arose. The sand slid whispering down from
the crest as he did so, but Levi was too intent in turning over
the contents of the chest to notice the slight sound.

Hiram's face was ghastly pale and drawn. For one moment he opened his lips as though to speak, but no word came.
So, white, silent, he stood for a few seconds, rather like a statue
than a living man, then, suddenly, his eyes fell upon the bag,
which Levi had brought with him, no doubt, to carry back the
treasure for which he and his companion were in search, and
which still lay spread out on the sand where it had been flung.
Then, as though a thought had suddenly flashed upon him, his
whole expression changed, his lips closed tightly together as
though fearing an involuntary sound might escape, and the
haggard look dissolved from his face.

Cautiously, slowly, he stepped over the edge of the sand
hill and down the slanting face. His coming was as silent as
death, for his feet made no noise as he sank ankle-deep in the
yielding surface. So, stealthily, step by step, he descended,
reached the bag, lifted it silently. Levi, still bending over the
chest and searching through the papers within, was not four
feet away. Hiram raised the bag in his hands. He must have
made some slight rustle as he did so, for suddenly Levi half
turned his head. But he was one instant too late. In a flash
the bag was over his head—shoulders—arms—body.

Then came another struggle, as fierce, as silent, as desperate
as that other—and as short. Wiry, tough, and strong as he was,
with a lean, sinewy, nervous vigor, fighting desperately for his
life as he was, Levi had no chance against the ponderous
strength of his stepbrother. In any case, the struggle could not
have lasted long; as it was, Levi stumbled backward over the
body of his dead mate and fell, with Hiram upon him. Maybe

he was stunned by the fall; maybe he felt the hopelessness of resistance, for he lay quite still while Hiram, kneeling upon him, drew the rope from the ring of the chest and, without uttering a word, bound it tightly around both the bag and the captive within, knotting it again and again and drawing it tight. Only once was a word spoken. "If you'll lemme go," said a muffled voice from the bag, "I'll give you five thousand pounds—it's in that there box." Hiram answered never a word, but continued knotting the rope and drawing it tight.

13

The *Scorpion* sloop-of-war lay in Lewes harbor all that winter and spring, probably upon the slim chance of a return of the pirates. It was about eight o'clock in the morning and Lieutenant Maynard was sitting in Squire Hall's office, fanning himself with his hat and talking in a desultory fashion. Suddenly the dim and distant noise of a great crowd was heard from without, coming nearer and nearer. The Squire and his visitor hurried to the door. The crowd was coming down the street shouting, jostling, struggling, some on the footway, some in the roadway. Heads were at the doors and windows, looking down upon them. Nearer they came, and nearer; then at last they could see that the press surrounded and accompanied one man. It was Hiram White, hatless, coatless, the sweat running down his face in streams, but stolid and silent as ever. Over his shoulder he carried a bag, tied round and round with a rope. It was not until the crowd and the man it surrounded had come quite near that the Squire and the lieutenant saw that a pair of legs in gray-yarn stockings hung from the bag. It was a man he was carrying.

Hiram had lugged his burden five miles that morning without help and with scarcely a rest on the way.

He came directly toward the Squire's office and, still sur-

193

rounded and hustled by the crowd, up the steep steps to the office within. He flung his burden heavily upon the floor without a word and wiped his streaming forehead.

The Squire stood with his knuckles on his desk, staring first at Hiram and then at the strange burden he had brought. A sudden hush fell upon all, though the voices of those without sounded as loud and turbulent as ever. "What is it, Hiram?" said Squire Hall at last.

Then for the first time Hiram spoke, panting thickly. "It's a bloody murderer," said he, pointing a quivering finger at the motionless figure.

"Here, some of you!" called out the Squire. "Come! Untie this man! Who is he?" A dozen willing fingers quickly unknotted the rope and the bag was slipped from the head and body.

Hair and face and eyebrows and clothes were powdered with meal, but, in spite of all and through all the innocent whiteness, dark spots and blotches and smears of blood showed upon head and arm and shirt. Levi raised himself upon his elbow and looked scowlingly around at the amazed, wonderstruck faces surrounding him.

"Why, it's Levi West!" croaked the Squire, at last finding his voice.

Then, suddenly, Lieutenant Maynard pushed forward, before the others crowded around the figure on the floor, and, clutching Levi by the hair, dragged his head backward so as to better see his face. "Levi West!" said he in a loud voice. "Is this the Levi West you've been telling me of? Look at that scar and the mark on his cheek! *This is Blueskin himself.*"

14

In the chest which Blueskin had dug up out of the sand were found not only the goldsmiths' bills taken from the

194

packet, but also many other valuables belonging to the officers and the passengers of the unfortunate ship.

The New York agents offered Hiram a handsome reward for his efforts in recovering the lost bills, but Hiram declined it, positively and finally. "All I want," said he, in his usual dull, stolid fashion, "is to have folks know I'm honest." Nevertheless, though he did not accept what the agents of the packet offered, fate took the matter into its own hands and rewarded him not unsubstantially. Blueskin was taken to England in the *Scorpion*. But he never came to trial. While in Newgate he hanged himself to the cell window with his own stockings. The news of his end was brought to Lewes in the early autumn and Squire Hall took immediate measures to have the five hundred pounds of his father's legacy duly transferred to Hiram.

In November Hiram married the pirate's widow.

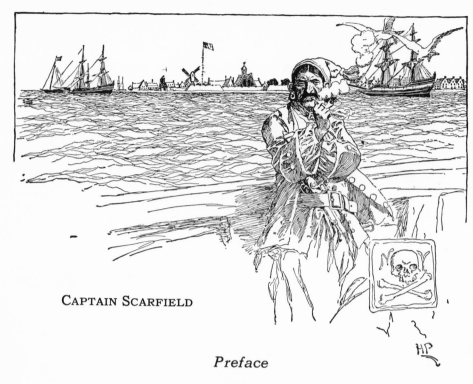

CAPTAIN SCARFIELD

Preface

The author of this narrative cannot recall that, in any history of the famous pirates, he has ever read a detailed and sufficient account of the life and death of Capt. John Scarfield. Doubtless some data concerning his death and the destruction of his schooner might be gathered from the report of Lieutenant Mainwaring, now filed in the archives of the Navy Department, but beyond such bald and bloodless narrative the author knows of nothing, unless it be the little chap-book history published by Isaiah Thomas in Newburyport about the year 1821–22, entitled, "A True History of the Life and Death of Captain Jack Scarfield." This lack of particularity in the history of one so notable in his profession it is the design of the present narrative in a measure to supply, and, if the author has seen fit to cast it in the form of a fictional story, it is only that it may make more easy reading for those who see fit to follow the tale from this to its conclusion.

So the Treasure Was Divided

VII

CAPTAIN SCARFIELD

1

LEAZER COOPER, or Captain Cooper, as was his better-known title in Philadelphia, was a prominent member of the Society of Friends. He was an overseer of the meeting and an occasional speaker upon particular occasions. When at home from one of his many voyages he never failed to occupy his seat in the meeting both on First Day and Fifth Day, and he was regarded by his fellow townsmen as a model of business integrity and of domestic responsibility.

More incidental to this history, however, it is to be narrated that Captain Cooper was one of those trading skippers who carried their own merchandise in their own vessels which they sailed themselves, and on whose decks they did their own bartering. His vessel was a swift, large schooner, the *Eliza Cooper, of Philadelphia,* named for his wife. His cruising grounds were the West India Islands, and his merchandise was flour and corn meal ground at the Brandywine Mills at Wilmington, Delaware.

During the War of 1812 he had earned, as was very well known, an extraordinary fortune in this trading; for flour and corn meal sold at fabulous prices in the French, Spanish, Dutch, and Danish islands, cut off, as they were, from the rest of the world by the British blockade.

The running of this blockade was one of the most hazardous

maritime ventures possible, but Captain Cooper had met with such unvaried success, and had sold his merchandise at such incredible profit that, at the end of the war, he found himself to have become one of the wealthiest merchants of his native city.

It was known at one time that his balance in the Mechanics' Bank was greater than that of any other individual depositor upon the books, and it was told of him that he had once deposited in the bank a chest of foreign silver coin, the exchanged value of which, when translated into American currency, was upward of forty-two thousand dollars—a prodigious sum of money in those days.

In person, Captain Cooper was tall and angular of frame. His face was thin and severe, wearing continually an unsmiling, masklike expression of continent and unruffled sobriety. His manner was dry and taciturn, and his conduct and life were measured to the most absolute accord with the teachings of his religious belief.

He lived in an old-fashioned house on Front Street below Spruce—as pleasant, cheerful a house as ever a trading captain could return to. At the back of the house a lawn sloped steeply down toward the river. To the south stood the wharf and storehouses; to the north an orchard and kitchen garden bloomed with abundant verdure. Two large chestnut trees sheltered the porch and the little space of lawn, and when you sat under them in the shade you looked down the slope between two rows of box bushes directly across the shining river to the Jersey shore.

At the time of our story—that is, about the year 1820—this property had increased very greatly in value, but it was the old home of the Coopers, as Eleazer Cooper was entirely rich enough to indulge his fancy in such matters. Accordingly, as he chose to live in the same house where his father and his grandfather had dwelt before him, he peremptorily, if quietly, refused all offers looking toward the purchase of the lot of ground—though it was now worth five or six times its former value.

As was said, it was a cheerful, pleasant home, impressing you when you entered it with the feeling of spotless and all-pervading cleanliness—a cleanliness that greeted you in the shining brass doorknocker; that entertained you in the sitting room with its stiff, leather-covered furniture, the brass-headed tacks whereof sparkled like so many stars—a cleanliness that bade you farewell in the spotless stretch of sand-sprinkled hallway, the wooden floor of which was worn into knobs around the nail heads by the countless scourings and scrubbings to which it had been subjected and which left behind them an all-pervading faint, fragrant odor of soap and warm water.

Eleazer Cooper and his wife were childless, but one inmate made the great, silent, shady house bright with life. Lucinda Fairbanks, a niece of Captain Cooper's by his only sister, was a handsome, sprightly girl of eighteen or twenty, and a great favorite in the Quaker society of the city.

It remains only to introduce the final and, perhaps, the most important actor of the narrative—Lieut. James Mainwaring. During the past twelve months or so he had been a frequent visitor at the Cooper house. At this time he was a broad-shouldered, red-cheeked, stalwart fellow of twenty-six or twenty-eight. He was a great social favorite, and possessed the added romantic interest of having been aboard the *Constitution* when she fought the *Guerriere*, and of having, with his own hands, touched the match that fired the first gun of that great battle.

Mainwaring's mother and Eliza Cooper had always been intimate friends, and the coming and going of the young man during his leave of absence were looked upon in the house as quite a matter of course. Half a dozen times a week he would drop in to execute some little commission for the ladies, or, if Captain Cooper was at home, to smoke a pipe of tobacco with him, to sip a dram of his famous old Jamaica rum, or to play a rubber of checkers of an evening. It is not likely that either of the older people was the least aware of the real cause of his visits; still less did they suspect that any passages of sentiment had passed between the young people.

The truth was that Mainwaring and the young lady were very deeply in love. It was a love that they were obliged to keep a profound secret, for not only had Eleazer Cooper held the strictest sort of testimony against the late war—a testimony so rigorous as to render it altogether unlikely that one of so military a profession as Mainwaring practiced could hope for his consent to a suit for marriage, but Lucinda could not have married one not a member of the Society of Friends without losing her own birthright membership therein. She herself might not attach much weight to such a loss of membership in the Society, but her fear of, and her respect for, her uncle led her to walk very closely in her path of duty in this respect. Accordingly she and Mainwaring met as they could—clandestinely—and the stolen moments were very sweet. With equal secrecy Lucinda had, at the request of her lover, sat for a miniature portrait to Mrs. Gregory, which miniature, set in a gold medallion, Mainwaring, with a mild, sentimental pleasure, wore hung around his neck and beneath his shirt frill next to his heart.

In the month of April of the year 1820 Mainwaring received orders to report at Washington. During the preceding autumn the West India pirates, and notably Capt. Jack Scarfield, had been more than usually active, and the loss of the packet *Marblehead* (which, sailing from Charleston, South Carolina, was never heard of more) was attributed to them.

Two other coasting vessels off the coast of Georgia had been looted and burned by Scarfield, and the government had at last aroused itself to the necessity of active measures for repressing these pests of the West India waters.

Mainwaring received orders to take command of the *Yankee,* a swift, light-draught, heavily armed brig of war, and to cruise about the Bahama Islands and to capture and destroy all the pirates' vessels he could there discover.

On his way from Washington to New York, where the *Yankee* was then waiting orders, Mainwaring stopped in Philadelphia to bid good-by to his many friends in that city. He called at the old Cooper House. It was on a Sunday afternoon. The spring was early and the weather extremely pleasant that day, being filled with a warmth almost as of summer. The apple trees were already in full bloom and filled all the air with their fragrance. Everywhere there seemed to be the pervading hum of bees, and the drowsy, tepid sunshine was very delightful.

At that time Eleazer was just home from an unusually successful voyage to Antigua. Mainwaring found the family sitting under one of the still leafless chestnut trees, Captain Cooper smoking his long clay pipe and lazily perusing a copy of the *National Gazette.* Eleazer listened with a great deal of interest to what Mainwaring had to say of his proposed cruise. He himself knew a great deal about the pirates, and, singularly unbending from his normal, stiff taciturnity, he began telling of what he knew, particularly of Captain Scarfield—in whom he appeared to take an extraordinary interest.

Vastly to Mainwaring's surprise, the old Quaker assumed the position of a defendant of the pirates, protesting that the wickedness of the accused was enormously exaggerated. He declared that he knew some of the freebooters very well and that at the most they were poor, misdirected wretches who had,

201

by easy gradation, slid into their present evil ways, from having been tempted by the government authorities to enter into
privateering in the days of the late war. He conceded that
Captain Scarfield had done many cruel and wicked deeds, but
he averred that he had also performed many kind and benevo-
lent actions. The world made no note of these latter, but took
care only to condemn the evil that had been done. He acknowledged that it was true that the pirate had allowed his
crew to cast lots for the wife and the daughter of the skipper
of the *Northern Rose,* but there were none of his accusers who
told how, at the risk of his own life and the lives of all his
crew, he had given succor to the schooner *Halifax,* found adrift
with all hands down with yellow fever. There was no defender
of his actions to tell how he and his crew of pirates had sailed
the pest-stricken vessel almost into the rescuing waters of
Kingston harbor. Eleazer confessed that he could not deny
that when Scarfield had tied the skipper of the *Baltimore Belle*
naked to the foremast of his own brig he had permitted his
crew of cutthroats (who were drunk at the time) to throw
bottles at the helpless captive, who died that night of the
wounds he had received. For this he was doubtless very justly
condemned, but who was there to praise him when he had, at
the risk of his life and in the face of the authorities, carried a
cargo of provisions which he himself had purchased at Tampa
Bay to the Island of Bella Vista after the great hurricane of
1818? In this notable adventure he had barely escaped, after
a two days' chase, the British frigate *Ceres,* whose captain, had
a capture been effected, would instantly have hung the unfortunate man to the yardarm in spite of the beneficent mis-
sion he was in the act of conducting.

In all this Eleazer had the air of conducting the case for the
defendant. As he talked he became more and more animated
and voluble. The light went out in his tobacco pipe, and a

hectic spot appeared in either thin and sallow cheek. Mainwaring sat wondering to hear the severely peaceful Quaker preacher defending so notoriously bloody and cruel a cutthroat pirate as Capt. Jack Scarfield. The warm and innocent surroundings, the old brick house looking down upon them, the odor of apple blossoms and the hum of bees seemed to make it all the more incongruous. And still the elderly Quaker skipper talked on and on with hardly an interruption, till the warm sun slanted to the west and the day began to decline.

That evening Mainwaring stayed to tea and when he parted from Lucinda Fairbanks it was after nightfall, with a clear, round moon shining in the milky sky and a radiance pallid and unreal enveloping the old house, the blooming apple trees, the sloping lawn and the shining river beyond. He implored his sweetheart to let him tell her uncle and aunt of their acknowledged love and to ask the old man's consent to it, but she would not permit him to do so. They were so happy as they were. Who knew but what her uncle might forbid their fondness? Would he not wait a little longer? Maybe it would all come right after a while. She was so fond, so tender, so tearful at the nearness of their parting that he had not the heart to insist. At the same time it was with a feeling almost of despair that he realized that he must now be gone—maybe for the space of two years—without in all that time possessing the right to call her his before the world.

When he bade farewell to the older people it was with a choking feeling of bitter disappointment. He yet felt the pressure of her cheek against his shoulder, the touch of soft and velvet lips to his own. But what were such clandestine endearments compared to what might, perchance, be his—the right of calling her his own when he was far away and upon the distant sea? And, besides, he felt like a coward who had shirked his duty.

But he was very much in love. The next morning appeared in a drizzle of rain that followed the beautiful warmth of the day before. He had the coach all to himself, and in the damp and leathery solitude he drew out the little oval picture from beneath his shirt frill and looked long and fixedly with a fond and foolish joy at the innocent face, the blue eyes, the red, smiling lips depicted upon the satinlike, ivory surface.

2

For the better part of five months Mainwaring cruised about in the waters surrounding the Bahama Islands. In that time he ran to earth and dispersed a dozen nests of pirates. He destroyed no less than fifteen piratical crafts of all sizes, from a large half-decked whaleboat to a three-hundred-ton barkentine. The name of the *Yankee* became a terror to every sea wolf in the western tropics, and the waters of the Bahama Islands became swept almost clean of the bloody wretches who had so lately infested it.

But the one freebooter of all others whom he sought—Capt. Jack Scarfield—seemed to evade him like a shadow, to slip through his fingers like magic. Twice he came almost within touch of the famous marauder, both times in the ominous wrecks that the pirate captain had left behind him. The first of these was the water-logged remains of a burned and still smoking wreck that he found adrift in the great Bahama channel. It was the *Water Witch, of Salem,* but he did not learn her tragic story until, two weeks later, he discovered a part of her crew at Port Maria, on the north coast of Jamaica. It was, indeed, a dreadful story to which he listened. The castaways said that they of all the vessel's crew had been spared so that they might tell the commander of the *Yankee,* should they meet him, that he might keep what he found, with Captain Scarfield's compliments, who served it up to him hot cooked.

204

Three weeks later he rescued what remained of the crew of the shattered, bloody hulk of the *Baltimore Belle,* eight of whose crew, headed by the captain, had been tied hand and foot and heaved overboard. Again, there was a message from Captain Scarfield to the commander of the *Yankee* that he might season what he found to suit his own taste.

Mainwaring was of a sanguine disposition, with fiery temper. He swore, with the utmost vehemence, that either he or John Scarfield would have to leave the earth.

He had little suspicion of how soon was to befall the ominous realization of his angry prophecy.

At that time one of the chief rendevous of the pirates was the little island of San Jose, one of the southernmost of the Bahama group. Here, in the days before the coming of the *Yankee,* they were wont to put in to careen and clean their vessels and to take in a fresh supply of provisions, gunpowder, and rum, preparatory to renewing their attacks upon the peaceful commerce circulating up and down outside the islands, or through the wide stretches of the Bahama channel.

Mainwaring had made several descents upon this nest of freebooters. He had already made two notable captures, and it was here he hoped eventually to capture Captain Scarfield himself.

A brief description of this one-time notorious rendezvous of freebooters might not be out of place. It consisted of a little settlement of those wattled and mud-smeared houses such as you find through the West Indies. There were only three houses of a more pretentious sort, built of wood. One of these was a storehouse, another was a rum shop, and a third a house in which dwelt a mulatto woman, who was reputed to be a sort of left-handed wife of Captain Scarfield's. The population was almost entirely black and brown. One or two Jews and a half dozen Yankee traders, of hardly dubious honesty, comprised the entire white population. The rest consisted of a mongrel accumulation of negroes and mulattoes and half-caste Spaniards, and of a multitude of black or yellow women and children. The settlement stood in a bight of the beach forming a small harbor and affording a fair anchorage for small vessels, excepting it were against the beating of a southeasterly gale. The houses, or cabins, were surrounded by clusters of coco palms and growths of bananas, and a long curve of white beach, sheltered from the large Atlantic breakers that burst and exploded upon an outer bar, was drawn like a necklace around the semicircle of emerald-green water.

Such was the famous pirates' settlement of San Jose—a paradise of nature and a hell of human depravity and wickedness—and it was to this spot that Mainwaring paid another visit a few days after rescuing the crew of the *Baltimore Belle* from her shattered and sinking wreck.

As the little bay with its fringe of palms and its cluster of wattle huts opened up to view, Mainwaring discovered a vessel lying at anchor in the little harbor. It was a large and well-rigged schooner of two hundred and fifty or three hundred tons burden. As the *Yankee* rounded to under the stern of the stranger and dropped anchor in such a position as to bring her broadside battery to bear should the occasion require, Mainwaring set his glass to his eye to read the name he could distinguish beneath the overhang of her stern. It is impossible to describe his infinite surprise when, the white lettering starting out in the circle of the glass, he read, *The Eliza Cooper, of Philadelphia.*

He could not believe the evidence of his senses. Certainly this sink of iniquity was the last place in the world he would have expected to have fallen in with Eleazer Cooper.

He ordered out the gig and had himself immediately rowed

206

over to the schooner. Whatever lingering doubts he might have entertained as to the identity of the vessel were quickly dispelled when he beheld Captain Cooper himself standing at the gangway to meet him. The impassive face of the friend showed neither surprise nor confusion at what must have been to him a most unexpected encounter.

But when he stepped upon the deck of the *Eliza Cooper* and looked about him, Mainwaring could hardly believe the evidence of his senses at the transformation that he beheld. Upon the main deck were eight twelve-pound carronade neatly covered with tarpaulin; in the bow a Long Tom, also snugly stowed away and covered, directed a veiled and muzzled snout out over the bowsprit.

It was entirely impossible for Mainwaring to conceal his astonishment at so unexpected a sight, and whether or not his own thoughts lent color to his imagination, it seemed to him that Eleazer Cooper concealed under the immobility of his countenance no small degree of confusion.

After Captain Cooper had led the way into the cabin and he and the younger man were seated over a pipe of tobacco and the invariable bottle of fine old Jamaica rum, Mainwaring made no attempt to refrain from questioning him as to the reason for this singular and ominous transformation.

"I am a man of peace, James Mainwaring," Eleazer replied, "but there are men of blood in these waters, and an appearance of great strength is of use to protect the innocent from the wicked. If I remained in appearance the peaceful trader I really am, how long does thee suppose I could remain unassailed in this place?"

It occurred to Mainwaring that the powerful armament he had beheld was rather extreme to be used merely as a preventive. He smoked for a while in silence and then he sud-

207

denly asked the other point-blank whether, if it came to blows with such a one as Captain Scarfield, would he make a fight of it?

The Quaker trading captain regarded him for a while in silence. His look, it seemed to Mainwaring, appeared to be dubitative as to how far he dared to be frank. "Friend James," he said at last, "I may as well acknowledge that my officers and crew are somewhat worldly. Of a truth they do not hold the same testimony as I. I am inclined to think that if it came to the point of a broil with those men of iniquity, my individual voice cast for peace would not be sufficient to keep my crew from meeting violence with violence. As for myself, thee knows who I am and what is my testimony in these matters."

Mainwaring made no comment as the extremely questionable manner in which the Quaker proposed to beat the devil about the stump. Presently he asked his second question:

"And might I inquire," he said, "what you are doing here and why you find it necessary to come at all into such a wicked, dangerous place as this?"

"Indeed, I knew thee would ask that question of me," said the Friend, "and I will be entirely frank with thee. These men of blood are, after all, but human beings, and as human beings they need food. I have at present upon this vessel upward of two hundred and fifty barrels of flour which will bring a higher price here than anywhere else in the West Indies. To be entirely frank with thee, I will tell thee that I was engaged in making a bargain for the sale of the greater part of my merchandise when the news of thy approach drove away my best customer."

Mainwaring sat for a while in smoking silence. What the other had told him explained many things he had not before understood. It explained why Captain Cooper got almost as much for his flour and corn meal now that peace had been declared as he had obtained when the war and the blockade were in full swing. It explained why he had been so strong a defender of Captain Scarfield and the pirates that afternoon in the garden. Meantime, what was to be done? Eleazer confessed openly that he dealt with the pirates. What now was his—Mainwaring's—duty in the case? Was the cargo of the *Eliza Cooper* contraband and subject to confiscation? And then another question framed itself in his mind: Who was this customer whom his approach had driven away?

As though he had formulated the inquiry into speech the other began directly to speak of it. "I know," he said, "that in a moment thee will ask me who was this customer of whom I have just now spoken. I have no desire to conceal his name from thee. It was the man who is known as Captain Jack or Captain John Scarfield."

Mainwaring fairly started from his seat. "The devil you say!" he cried. "And how long has it been," he asked, "since he left you?"

The Quaker skipper carefully refilled his pipe, which he had by now smoked out. "I would judge," he said, "that it is a matter of four or five hours since news was brought overland by means of swift runners of thy approach. Immediately the man of wickedness disappeared." Here Eleazer set the bowl of his pipe to the candle flame and began puffing out voluminous clouds of smoke. "I would have thee understand, James Mainwaring," he resumed, "that I am no friend of this wicked and sinful man. His safety is nothing to me. It is only a question of buying upon his part and of selling upon mine. If it is any satisfaction to thee I will heartily promise to bring thee news if I hear anything of the man of Belial. I may furthermore say that I think it is likely thee will have news more or less directly of him within the space of a day. If this should happen, however, thee will have to do thy own fighting without help

209

from me, for I am no man of combat nor of blood and will take no hand in it either way."

It struck Mainwaring that the words contained some meaning that did not appear upon the surface. This significance struck him as so ambiguous that when he went aboard the *Yankee* he confided as much of his suspicions as he saw fit to his second in command, Lieutenant Underwood. As night descended he had a double watch set and had everything prepared to repel any attack or surprise that might be attempted.

3

Nighttime in the tropics descends with a surprising rapidity. At one moment the earth is shining with the brightness of the twilight; the next, as it were, all things are suddenly swallowed into a gulf of darkness. The particular night of which this story treats was not entirely clear; the time of year was about the approach of the rainy season, and the tepid, tropical clouds added obscurity to the darkness of the sky, so that the night fell with even more startling quickness than usual. The blackness was very dense. Now and then a group of drifting stars swam out of a rift in the vapors, but the night was curiously silent and of a velvety darkness.

As the obscurity had deepened, Mainwaring had ordered lanthorns to be lighted and slung to the shrouds and to the stays, and the faint yellow of their illumination lighted the level white of the snug little war vessel, gleaming here and there in a starlike spark upon the brass trimmings and causing the rows of cannons to assume curiously gigantic proportions.

For some reason Mainwaring was possessed by a strange, uneasy feeling. He walked restlessly up and down the deck for a time, and then, still full of anxieties for he knew not what, went into his cabin to finish writing up his log for the day. He unstrapped his cutlass and laid it upon the table, lighted his pipe at the lanthorn and was about preparing to lay aside his coat when word was brought to him that the captain of the trading schooner was come alongside and had some private information to communicate to him.

Mainwaring surmised in an instant that the trader's visit related somehow to news of Captain Scarfield, and as immediately, in the relief of something positive to face, all of his feeling of restlessness vanished like a shadow of mist. He gave orders that Captain Cooper should be immediately shown into the cabin, and in a few moments the tall, angular form of the Quaker skipper appeared in the narrow, lanthorn-lighted space.

Mainwaring at once saw that his visitor was strangely agitated and disturbed. He had taken off his hat, and shining beads of perspiration had gathered and stood clustered upon his forehead. He did not reply to Mainwaring's greeting; he did not, indeed, seem to hear it; but he came directly forward to the table and stood leaning with one hand upon the open log book in which the lieutenant had just been writing. Mainwaring had reseated himself at the head of the table, and the tall figure of the skipper stood looking down at him as from a considerable height.

"James Mainwaring," he said, "I promised thee to report if I had news of the pirate. Is thee ready now to hear my news?"

There was something so strange in his agitation that it began to infect Mainwaring with a feeling somewhat akin to that which appeared to disturb his visitor. "I know not what you mean, sir!" he cried, "by asking if I care to hear your news. At this moment I would rather have news of that scoundrel than to have anything I know of in the world."

"Thou would? Thou would?" cried the other, with mounting agitation. "Is thee in such haste to meet him as all that?

211

Very well; very well, then. Suppose I could bring thee face to face with him—what then? Hey? Hey? Face to face with him, James Mainwaring!"

The thought instantly flashed into Mainwaring's mind that the pirate had returned to the island; that perhaps at that moment he was somewhere near at hand.

"I do not understand you, sir," he cried. "Do you mean to tell me that you know where the villain is? If so, lose no time in informing me, for every instant of delay may mean his chance of again escaping."

"No danger of that!" the other declared, vehemently. "No danger of that! I'll tell thee where he is and I'll bring thee to him quick enough!" And as he spoke he thumped his fist against the open log book. In the vehemence of his growing excitement his eyes appeared to shine green in the lanthorn light, and the sweat that had stood in beads upon his forehead was now running in streams down his face. One drop hung like a jewel to the tip of his beaklike nose. He came a step nearer to Mainwaring and bent forward toward him, and there was something so strange and ominous in his bearing that the lieutenant instinctively drew back a little where he sat.

"Captain Scarfield sent something to you," said Eleazer, almost in a raucous voice, "something that you will be surprised to see." And the lapse in his speech from the Quaker "thee" to the plural "you" struck Mainwaring as singularly strange.

As he was speaking Eleazer was fumbling in a pocket of his long-tailed drab coat, and presently he brought something forth that gleamed in the lanthorn light.

The next moment Mainwearing saw leveled directly in his face the round and hollow nozzle of a pistol.

There was an instant of dead silence and then, "I am the man you seek!" said Eleazer Cooper, in a tense and breathless voice.

Then the Real Fight Began

The whole thing had happened so instantaneously and un-expectedly that for the moment Mainwaring sat like one petri-fied. Had a thunderbolt fallen from the silent sky and burst at his feet he could not have been more stunned. He was like one held in the meshes of a horrid nightmare, and he gazed as through a mist of impossibility into the lineaments of the well-known, sober face now transformed as from within into the aspect of a devil. That face, now ashy white, was distorted into a diabolical grin. The teeth glistened in the lamplight. The brows, twisted into a tense and convulsed frown, were drawn down into black shadows, through which the eyes burned a baleful green like the eyes of a wild animal driven to bay. Again he spoke in the same breathless voice. "I am John Scar-field! Look at me, then, if you want to see a pirate!" Again there was a little time of silence, through which Mainwaring heard his watch ticking loudly from where it hung against the bulkhead. Then once more the other began speaking. "You would chase me out of the West Indies, would you? G——— you! What are you come to now? You are caught in your own trap, and you'll squeal loud enough before you get out of it. Speak a word or make a movement and I'll blow your brains out against the partition behind you! Listen to what I say or you are a dead man. Sing out an order instantly for my mate and my bos'n to come here to the cabin, and be quick about it, for my finger's on the trigger, and it's only a pull to shut your mouth forever."

It was astonishing to Mainwaring, in afterward thinking about it all, how quickly his mind began to recover its steadi-ness after that first astonishing shock. Even as the other was speaking he discovered that his brain was becoming clarified to a wonderful lucidity; his thoughts were becoming rear-ranged, and with a marvelous activity and an alertness he had never before experienced. He knew that if he moved to escape

213

or uttered any outcry he would be instantly a dead man, for the circle of the pistol barrel was directed full against his forehead and with the steadiness of a rock. If he could but for an instant divert that fixed and deadly attention he might still have a chance for life. With the thought an inspiration burst into his mind and he instantly put it into execution; thought, inspiration, and action, as in a flash, were one. He must make the other turn aside his deadly gaze, and instantly he roared out in a voice that stunned his own ears: "Strike, bos'n! Strike, quick!"

Taken by surprise, and thinking, doubtless, that another enemy stood behind him, the pirate swung around like a flash with his pistol leveled against the blank boarding. Equally upon the instant he saw the trick that had been played upon him and in a second flash had turned again. The turn and return had occupied but a moment of time, but that moment, thanks to the readiness of his own invention, had undoubtedly saved Mainwaring's life. As the other turned away his gaze for that brief instant Mainwaring leaped forward and upon him. There was a flashing flame of fire as the pistol was discharged and a deafening detonation that seemed to split his brain. For a moment, with reeling senses, he supposed himself to have been shot, the next he knew he had escaped. With the energy of despair he swung his enemy around and drove him with prodigious violence against the corner of the table. The pirate emitted a grunting cry and then they fell together, Mainwaring upon the top, and the pistol clattered with them to the floor in their fall. Even he he fell, Mainwaring roared in a voice of thunder, "All hands repel boarders!" And then again, "All hands repel boarders!"

Whether hurt by the table edge or not, the fallen pirate struggled as though possessed of forty devils, and in a moment or two Mainwaring saw the shine of a long, keen knife that he had drawn from somewhere about his person. The lieutenant caught him by the wrist, but the other's muscles were as though made of steel. They both fought in despairing silence, the one to carry out his frustrated purposes to kill, the other to save his life. Again and again Mainwaring felt that the knife had been thrust against him, piercing once his arm, once his shoulder, and again his neck. He felt the warm blood streaming down his arm and body and looked about him in despair. The pistol lay near upon the deck of the cabin. Still holding the other by the wrist as he could, Mainwaring snatched up the empty weapon and struck once and again at the bald, narrow forehead beneath him. A third blow he delivered with all the force he could command, and then with a violent and convulsive throe the straining muscles beneath him relaxed and grew limp and the fight was won.

Through all the struggle he had been aware of the shouts of voices, of trampling of feet and discharge of firearms, and the thought came to him, even through his own danger, that the *Yankee* was being assaulted by the pirates. As he felt the struggling form beneath him loosen and dissolve into quietude, he leaped up, and snatching his cutlass, which still lay upon the table, rushed out upon the deck, leaving the stricken form lying twitching upon the floor behind him.

It was a fortunate thing that he had set double watches and prepared himself for some attack from the pirates, otherwise the *Yankee* would certainly have been lost. As it was, the surprise was so overwhelming that the pirates, who had been concealed in the large whaleboat that had come alongside, were not only able to gain a foothold upon the deck, but for a time it seemed as though they would drive the crew of the brig below the hatches.

But as Mainwaring, streaming with blood, rushed out upon the deck, the pirates became immediately aware that their own

215

captain must have been overpowered, and in an instant their desperate energy began to evaporate. One or two jumped overboard; one, who seemed to be the mate, fell dead from a pistol shot, and then, in the turn of a hand, there was a rush of a retreat and a vision of leaping forms in the dusky light of the lanthorns and a sound of splashing in the water below.

The crew of the *Yankee* continued firing at the phosphorescent wakes of the swimming bodies, but whether with effect it was impossible at the time to tell.

4

The pirate captain did not die immediately. He lingered for three or four days, now and then unconscious, now and then semiconscious, but always deliriously wandering. All the while he thus lay dying, the mulatto woman, with whom he lived in this part of his extraordinary dual existence, nursed and cared for him with such rude attentions as the surroundings afforded. In the wanderings of his mind the same duality of life followed him. Now and then he would appear the calm, sober, self-contained, well-ordered member of a peaceful society that his friends in his far-away home knew him to be; at other times the nether part of his nature would leap up into life like a wild beast, furious and gnashing. At the one time he talked evenly and clearly of peaceful things; at the other time he blasphemed and hooted with fury.

Several time Mainwaring, though racked by his own wounds, sat beside the dying man through the silent watches of the tropical nights. Oftentimes upon these occasions as he looked at the thin, lean face babbling and talking so aimlessly, he wondered what it all meant. Could it have been madness —madness in which the separate entities of good and bad each had, in its turn, a perfect and distinct existence? He chose to think that this was this was the case. Who, within his inner

216

consciousness, does not feel that same ferine, savage man struggling against the stern, adamantine bonds of morality and decorum? Were those bonds burst asunder, as it was with this man, might not the wild beast rush forth, as it had rushed forth in him, to rend and to tear? Such were the questions that Mainwaring asked himself. And how had it all come about? By what easy gradations had the respectable Quaker skipper descended from the decorum of his home life, step by step, into such a gulf of iniquity? Many such thoughts passed through Mainwaring's mind, and he pondered them through the still reaches of the tropical nights while he sat watching the pirate captain struggle out of the world he had so long burdened. At last the poor wretch died, and the earth was well quit of one of its torments.

A systematic search was made through the island for the scattered crew, but none was captured. Either there were some secret hiding places upon the island (which was not very likely) or else they had escaped in boats hidden somewhere among the tropical foliage. At any rate they were gone.

Nor, search as he would, could Mainwaring find a trace of any of the pirate treasure. After the pirate's death and under close questioning, the weeping mulatto woman so far broke down as to confess in broken English that Captain Scarfield had taken a quantity of silver money aboard his vessel, but either she was mistaken or else the pirates had taken it thence again and had hidden it somewhere else.

Nor would the treasure ever have been found but for a most fortuitous accident.

Mainwaring had given orders that the *Eliza Cooper* was to be burned, and a party was detailed to carry the order into execution. At this the cook of the *Yankee* came petitioning for some of the Wilmington and Brandywine flour to make some plum duff upon the morrow, and Mainwaring granted his re-

217

quest in so far that he ordered one of the men to knock open one of the barrels of flour and to supply the cook's demands.

The crew detailed to execute this modest order in connection with the destruction of the pirate vessel had not been gone a quarter of an hour when word came back that the hidden treasure had been found.

Mainwaring hurried aboard the *Eliza Cooper,* and there in the midst of the open flour barrel he beheld a great quantity of silver coin buried in and partly covered by the white meal. A systematic search was now made. One by one the flour barrels were heaved up from below and burst open on the deck and their contents searched, and if nothing but the meal was found it was swept overboard. The breeze was whitened with clouds of flour, and the white meal covered the surface of the ocean for yards around.

In all, upward of one hundred and fifty thousand dollars was found concealed beneath the innocent flour and meal. It was no wonder the pirate captain was so successful, when he could upon an instant's notice transform himself from a wolf of the ocean to a peaceful Quaker trader selling flour to the hungry towns and settlements among the scattered islands of the West Indies, and so carrying his bloody treasure safely into his quiet Northern home.

In concluding this part of the narrative it may be added that a wide strip of canvas painted black was discovered in the hold of the *Eliza Cooper.* Upon it, in great white letters, was painted the name, "The Bloodhound." Undoubtedly this was used upon occasions to cover the real and peaceful title of the trading schooner, just as its captain had, in reverse, covered his sanguine and cruel life by a thin sheet of morality and respectability.

This is the true story of the death of Capt. Jack Scarfield. The Newburyport chap-book, of which I have already spoken, speaks only of how the pirate disguised himself upon the ocean as a Quaker trader.

Nor is it likely that anyone ever identified Eleazer Cooper with the pirate, for only Mainwaring of all the crew of the *Yankee* was exactly aware of the true identity of Captain Scarfield. All that was ever known to the world was that Eleazer Cooper had been killed in a fight with the pirates.

In a little less than a year Mainwaring was married to Lucinda Fairbanks. As to Eleazer Cooper's fortune, which eventually came into the possession of Mainwaring through his wife, it was many times a subject of speculation to the lieutenant how it had been earned. There were times when he felt well assured that a part of it at least was the fruit of piracy, but it was entirely impossible to guess how much more was the result of legitimate trading.

For a little time it seemed to Mainwaring that he should give it all up, but this was at once so impracticable and so quixotic that he presently abandoned it, and in time his qualms and misdoubts faded away and he settled himself down to enjoy that which had come to him through his marriage.

In time the Mainwarings removed to New York, and ultimately the fortune that the pirate Scarfield had left behind him was used in part to found the great shipping house of Mainwaring & Bigot, whose famous transatlantic packet ships were in their time the admiration of the whole world.

THE END

Format by Kohar Alexanian
Set in Linotype Bookman
Composed by Westcott & Thomson, Inc.
Printed by Murray Printing Company
Bound by Haddon Bindery
Harper & Row, Publishers, Incorporated